GW00775666

The Pheasant

The Pheasant

Ecology, Management and Conservation

David Hill *and* Peter Robertson

BSP PROFESSIONAL BOOKS

OXFORD LONDON EDINBURGH

BOSTON PALO ALTO MELBOURNE

Copyright © David Hill and Peter
Robertson, 1988

All rights reserved. No part of this
publication may be reproduced,
stored in a retrieval system, or
transmitted, in any form or by any
means, electronic, mechanical,
photocopying, recording or otherwise
without the prior permission of the
copyright owner.

First published 1988

British Library
Cataloguing in Publication Data
Hill, David
  The pheasant.
  1. Livestock : Pheasants
  I. Title II. Robertson, Peter
  636.5'94

ISBN 0−632−02011−3

BSP Professional Books
A division of Blackwell Scientific
  Publications Ltd
Editorial Offices:
Osney Mead, Oxford OX2 OEL
  (Orders: Tel. 0865 240201)
8 John Street, London WC1N 2ES
23 Ainslie Place, Edinburgh EH3 6AJ
3 Cambridge Center, Suite 208,
  Cambridge, MA 02142, USA
667 Lytton Avenue, Palo Alto,
  California 94301, USA
107 Barry Street, Carlton, Victoria
  3053, Australia

Set by Setrite Typesetters Ltd
Printed and bound in Great Britain by
Mackays of Chatham PLC, Kent

Contents

Preface

The summer of 1982 saw both authors separately and unknowingly preparing to start work on a rather unusual bird, the pheasant.

In Britain the Game Conservancy had just initiated its 'Pheasants in the Wild' project when David Hill finished his DPhil on the population dynamics of wildfowl at the Edward Grey Institute, Oxford University. He moved to Fordingbridge to head the project in the late summer of 1982. Meanwhile, an Irish hunting organisation, The National Association of Regional Game Councils, had agreed to fund a PhD student to investigate the success of releasing hand-reared birds. Peter Robertson finished college at Reading and caught the ferry to Dublin. Exactly who started fieldwork first remains a matter of debate.

It was Owen Lee, a mutual friend, who made the connection between the two of us and a correspondence began, often over the most appalling telephone lines imaginable. It was the summer of 1983 before we both actually met, a day spent radiotracking on the Damerham study area and crowing at cock pheasants to see their response (rather a puzzled one in the main). We exchanged a great many ideas that day.

The telephone calls continued until Pete finished his fieldwork in 1985. With excellent timing, David obtained a grant from the Forestry Commission and offered Pete a post-doctoral research assistantship. We were also joined by a number of contract assistants who took on various aspects of the work. Shortly afterwards the 'Pheasants in the Wild' project was expanded into the existing 'Pheasants and Woodlands Project', which allowed us to focus a great deal of our efforts on researching the habitat requirements of pheasants whilst using woodland cover. The Forestry Commission were most interested in this aspect.

This book was started shortly after the launch of the new project when David realised that our combined efforts and research experiences might be made available to a wider readership. The time from first putting pen to paper until submission took two years. More than a few sleepless nights were had by both of us and yet we had surprisingly few disagreements.

Halfway through writing, David left the Game Conservancy and took the opportunity of joining the Reserves Division of the Royal Society for the Protection of Birds. Once again communication was over the phone, although the lines were infinitely better this time.

In the end this book represents nearly ten man-years of work by us both together, with numerous years by other workers and six or so man-years by our contract staff. It describes the pheasant, its natural history, and the way it has adapted to the changing farming landscape and looks forward to the wider implications for countryside management. It will be of interest to both professional and amateur ornithologists, to landowners, and to all those with an interest in the countryside. We have both gained a great deal of pleasure from studying this animal in its wild, if indeed not 'natural', environment, but we would be the first to point out that the pheasant has many more man-years of study left in it.

David Hill and Peter Robertson
January 1988

Acknowledgements

We are indebted to the many people who have enabled this project to reach completion. During the period 1979 to 1983 Matt Ridley carried out some invaluable research into the mating system of pheasants whilst at the Edward Grey Institute, Oxford University. We thank him sincerely for many enthusiastic discussions and for allowing us to use some of his data throughout this book.

The majority of this work was carried out at The Game Conservancy's headquarters in Fordingbridge. We are especially indebted to the Director, Richard Van Oss, and to the Director of Research, G.R. Potts, for their advice and enthusiasm during the course of these studies. Quite a number of people have assisted us in the field, and we give particular thanks to Clive Bealey, Caroline Beckett, Clare Ludolf, Alison McWhinney, Noelle Power, Kathleen Raw, Mike Swan, Julian Thompson, Maureen Woodburn and Lewellyn Young. Steve Moreby is the best faecal analyst in the business and we thank him for his hard work. Brian Creswell of Biotrack kindly gave advice on radio-telemetry and built our radiotags.

Our endeavours would have been impossible without the tremendous support and interest of a number of landowners. John Hayward and Roy Shepherd gave us complete access to their farms, and their colleagues, John Hooper and Ken Sims, helped us in many ways, as did Hugh Oliver-Bellasis of Manydown Estate. Professor I. Gordon and Mr S. Bowie provided facilities on Lyons Estate in Ireland. John Williams of Rockstead estate also gave us support. We wish to thank Lord Shaftesbury for allowing us to work at Wimborne St Giles and Don Ford, the Head Keeper, for his patient help, particularly during our early morning and late evening radiotracking. John Reynolds of Waterbeach also deserves thanks for enabling our Ph.D student to conduct research on his farm. Liam Nolan offered marvellous hospitality on the Ardbrae Estate in Co. Wicklow. During our visits to shoots we were made most welcome by the Duke and Duchess of Grafton at Euston Hall, Colonel Sir John Ruggles-Brise and his family at Spains Hall, Oscar Colburn at Crickley Barrow, Richard Baker at Bustard Farm, David Woodman on the Ashburnham Estate, Dick Riddle and family of Cobley, Dan Tanner at Edmondsham, and Andrew Christie-Miller of Clarendon Park. Andrew Christie-Miller is also chairman of the Pheasants and Woodlands Research Project steering committee. He, and other members of the committee, The Hon. J.M.E. Bruce, O. Colburn, J.M.P.H. Evelyn, Sir Leonard Figg, Rob Fuller, Rod Hewitt, Hanslip Long, Ian Odin, The Earl Peel, Phil Ratcliffe, Rod Stern, R. Turner and J.J.I. Whitaker, have spent many hours with us talking over our work and giving us the value of their experiences in forestry and conservation.

We have always been surrounded by colleagues off whom to bounce ideas and to approach for advice, and we would like to thank them for their contributions: Mark Anderson, Hugh Brazier, Douglas Butler, Nick Carter, Charles Eldam, Pete Garson, Mike Gill, Pete Hudson, David Jackson, Ian Lindsay, Ian McCall, Ron MacDonald, Chris Minchin, Dave Newborn, Richard Prior, Mike Rands, Noel Reid, Hugo Straker, Mike Swan, Martin Tickler, John Whelan and Kevin Wissett-Warner.

Throughout our studies we have been most fortunate to have had the cooperation of a number of universities and we would especially like to thank Professor Sir Richard Southwood and Chris Perrins of Oxford, Jim Curry, Paddy Brennan, Gwylym Evans and John Whelan of University College Dublin, Professor Gordon Conway, Denis Wright and John Mumford of Imperial College and Rory Putman of Southampton. Raymond O'Connor and David Glue of the British Trust for Ornithology kindly gave us permission to use data from the nest recording scheme.

We would like to thank the Game Conservancy for allowing us access to their black and white photographic library.

We have been most grateful for the sound advice offered and the help received from six colleagues in particular. They deserve special mention for the influence they have had on our careers and research interests: Dick Potts, Steve Tapper, Ian Newton, Chris Perrins, Nick Sotherton and David Jenkins. Three other people are sadly no longer with us, Nigel Gray, Terence Blank and Jimmy Hamilton. We wish to thank them for all their help and patience.

Little of this work would have been possible without our financial sponsors. The Game Conservancy, Forestry Commission, the National Association of Regional Game Councils, the Country Land-owners Association, *Shooting Times*, Irish Forestry and Wildlife Service, University College Dublin, the Royal Society for the Protection of Birds and the W.G. Cadbury Trust, supported us financially in a number of ways.

Many thanks are due to our excellent secretaries Patsy Hitchings, Corinne Duggins and Phillipa Bond for their help in preparing some of the manuscript. We would also like to pay special thanks to those colleagues who gave up their time to read and correct various drafts for us. They were Dick Potts, Steve Tapper, Mike Swan, Clare Ludolf, Robert Kenward, Chris Perrins, Kevin Bayes, Patrick Osborne, and Andrew Christie-Miller.

Our publishers and their staff, particularly Julian Grover and Richard Miles, have helped us through this project with much appreciated advice. We are also indebted to our great friend Esdaile Hudson for his fine artwork on the cover and throughout the text.

Finally we would sincerely like to thank our respective ladies, Kathleen and Noelle, for their unquestioning support whilst our heads were buried in data in the pursuit of the private life of the pheasant.

1   Introduction

Why should anyone wish to write a book about the pheasant? It is certainly not a rare bird. In fact, some people would claim that it is not a 'real' bird at all, it having been introduced to most of Europe and North America. Furthermore, its importance as a gamebird and the fact that many sportsmen augment their populations with hand-reared birds leads many people to view the pheasant as an entirely artificial member of our avifauna. This is reflected in its popularity: although close to the hearts of many hunters this species was recently voted 'the most hated bird in Britain' at a birdwatchers' conference.

How many more reasons should we give to justify our interest in this species? One thing is certainly clear — for such a common bird it is very poorly understood.

There are a number of other reasons for writing this book. The male pheasant is a superbly beautiful creature, as exemplified by the words of Alexander Pope:

Ah! what avails his glossy, varying dyes,
His purpled crest, and scarlet circled eyes,
The vivid green his shining plumes unfold,
His painted wings and breast that flames with gold.

The pheasant also has a fascinating breeding system. Males establish territories in the spring which they actively defend. Their displays at this time are colourful and dramatic. The fact that they display in the same way in marshy clearings in their native China makes them an even more respectable species to study. Each territorial male attempts to attract a number of females to his 'harem' although he takes no part in incubation nor in raising the chicks. This breeding system, known as harem defence polygyny, is the rarest breeding strategy used by any bird, shared with only a handful of other species.

A further reason for working on pheasants is the vast amount of money spent on their management. In 1981 it was estimated that game shooting in Britain, which is largely comprised of pheasant shooting, was worth nearly £400 million per year. This is (in today's figures) more than ten times the entire budget of the Nature Conservancy Council, the government's watchdog on conservation!

This book follows the life cycle of the pheasant. We have tried to review work on this bird from around the world, with special reference to North America. However, we rely to a large extent on our own studies to describe the fine detail of the pheasant's life history and to relate its management to changes in the British countryside. Despite the large volume of work on the pheasant, much of it only deals with the return rates of hand-reared birds or nest-site selection. Pheasants are easily reared and many people have not seen the benefit of researching pheasant ecology, apart from learning how best to pour reared birds into the environment.

The second chapter deals with the main areas on which our

pheasant studies were carried out, together with the techniques used to study them. After this we follow the pheasants' life cycle, describing its natural history and the impact of its management on both the bird itself and the countryside as a whole.

Once the stubbles have been ploughed, pheasants move back into areas of permanent cover, or, in the case of the open fenlands of Britain and cornbelt of the United States, to ditches, dykes or meagre fencelines holding some dead residual cover. Using radio-telemetry and counting techniques we have built up a picture of the pheasants' ecology in winter and this is described in Chapter 3.

Once winter is over, any snows have melted and just before the trees bear bud, pheasants undertake exploratory movements, and the aggressive behaviour and territory establishment of males, which lies dormant during the winter months, gains pace and becomes a prominent sight in spring. In Chapter 4 we describe the business of finding mates, detailing the unusual mating system in which the males attract a harem of hens to their territories and guard them from the risks of rape or injury from other males, as well as keeping an eye out for predators.

Once the females have mated they incubate their clutch of eggs relying on their cryptic plumage for concealment. However, as we shall show in Chapter 5, predation is still an important aspect of pheasant ecology. We re-examine nest data from a number of large-scale American studies and compare them with data collected in Britain, both from a series of voluntary nest record schemes and from our own radiotracking. Some hens parasitise the nests of other pheasants by laying their eggs in them. We suggest in Chapter 5 that, far from being a random event, this is a strategy on the part of the parasitising female which can benefit her at the expense of her host.

When the eggs hatch, the chicks leave the nest almost immediately and search for insect food. In Chapter 6 we describe how insects are crucial to a chicks' chances of survival. Modern cereal monocultures, which receive huge quantities of pesticides, create hostile conditions for both invertebrates and gamebird chicks. In Chapter 6 we describe chick diet, survival and dependence on insects in these habitats.

In the middle of summer, large numbers of estates in Britain release pheasant poults from pens in preparation for the start of the shooting season. Poults are used in a similar way in North

America, althought the period in the release pen is either non-existent or of shortened duration. Large amounts of money are spent in providing birds to shoot and in Chapter 7 we describe the process of hand-rearing. We avoid going into the practical details of establishing a 'hand-reared shoot' which are detailed in other books. We discuss how hand-reared birds appear to lack any instinctive or innate sense of anti-predator avoidance and how this affects their survival, management and breeding success.

The shooting season is what pheasant management is really aimed at. The poults are then old enough to be shot and if it has been a good breeding season then the wild birds make a significant contribution to the bag. In Chapter 8 we outline the role of shooting and its effect on populations of pheasants. We take a historical look at a number of prime pheasant estates and ask how dependent are the modern shoots on hand-reared birds. Finally in this chapter we develop a simple computer simulation model constructed from data collected from our studies in order to determine levels of maximum sustainable yield, that is the number and proportion of birds which could be shot without detrimental effects on the size of the bag in the next year. Such models have shortcomings but they do enable us to focus our attentions on potentially important questions and areas for future research.

In Chapter 9 we address aspects of managing pheasants and their habitats through the ages. Ever since pheasants were managed for organised shoots, predatory species have been controlled by gamekeepers, an activity which has brought its fair share of controversy. We discuss the importance of various species to the pheasant and the effects of gamekeepers on their numbers.

Traditional woodland management has been good for pheasants by providing the main source of cover and shelter. We describe both traditional and modern methods of woodland management in order to show how they fit into the pattern of the working estate which includes game management.

Dramatic changes have occurred in the British landscape since the Second World War. Indeed, one way Europe responded to the war was by creating greater crop yields. Habitats were lost and fields could no longer fill with the flowers of summer weeds on which live many insects useful to game chicks. Gamekeeping also declined as hand-rearing techniques were refined to enable fewer staff to cope with more birds. We document the changing countryside not only from the point of view of agriculture but also in terms of changes in pheasant management. Finally in Chapter 9 we look to the future and outline new techniques based on game research which could help redress the balance in the countryside.

Game management is not always seen as good for conservation. While large-scale hand-rearing and the reduction of public access may cause problems we feel that the common ground between game management and conservation far outweighs any differences and in Chapter 10 we attempt to bridge this gap. Pheasant management can be extremely good for wildlife, and if done correctly it offers, we suggest, a unique opportunity for a countryside 'industry' to pay for conservation in the lowland forest and agricultural environment where profit and finance usually have the last say.

If we are to achieve a more varied, diverse and pleasant landscape in the lowlands of Britain, we need a policy which seriously alters the way we use land. We know that pheasants are only a small part of our rural environment but whilst conservation organisations push for land purchase and site designation as a means of protecting the last remaining land of special conservation value, interest in pheasants as a game species is becoming much wider and their potential for influencing land-use in the countryside as a whole should not be undervalued. This is our message.

NATIVE RANGE AND SUBSPECIES

The native range of the pheasant spreads from the eastern shore of the Black Sea to the Caspian and along its southern shore. Its distribution then extends eastwards along the northern slopes of the Himalayas, spreading northwards into Manchuria and Korea, southwards to the borders of Vietnam. Pheasants are also found on Taiwan and the Japanese archipelago. The natural and introduced ranges of the pheasant are shown in Fig. 1.1.

There are two species of true pheasants, the common pheasant *Phasianus colchicus* and the Japanese green pheasant *Phasianus versicolor*. These species contain thirty and two subspecies respectively.

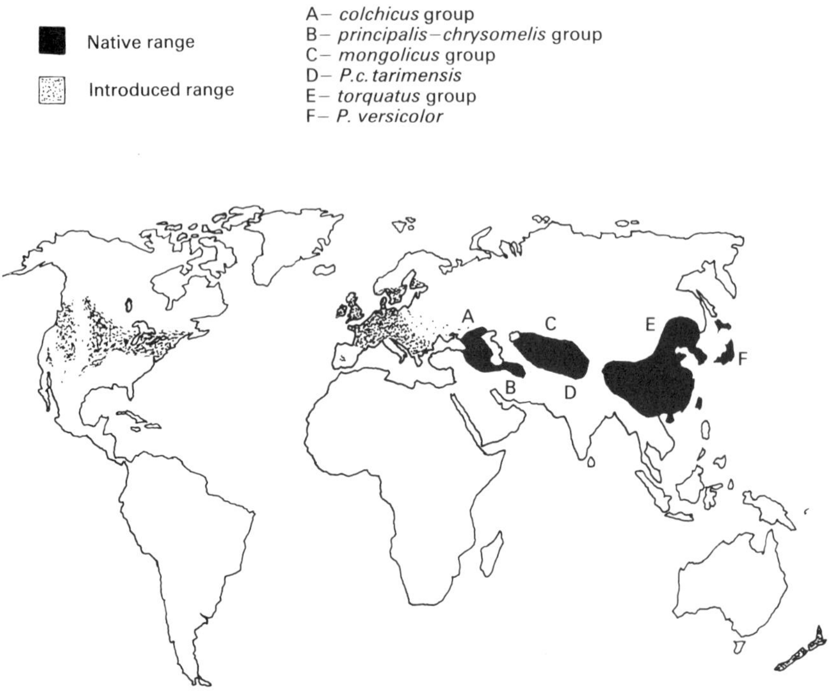

Fig. 1.1 The native and introduced ranges of the pheasant showing the locations of the main sub-specific groups. Pheasants within their introduced ranges are a conglomerate of different subspecies. Adapted from Delacour (1977), Long (1981) and Johnsgard (1986).

There are five groups of subspecies of *P. colchicus*, separated mainly by differences in the plumages of the male and by their geographic distribution:

(a) The *colchicus* group − known as black-necked pheasants, in which the males are purplish with light brown or buff wing coverts and no trace of a white neck ring.

Phasianus colchicus colchicus	Black-necked
P.c. septentrionalis	Northern Caucasian
P.c. talischensis	Talisch Caucasian
P.c. persicus	Persian

(b) The *principalis-chrysomelis* group − known as the white-winged pheasants. These subspecies are similar to the *colchicus* group but have pure white wing coverts and tend towards a redder, maroon plumage. Some have a partial white neck ring.

P.c. principalis	Prince of Wales
P.c. zarudnyi	Zarudny's
P.c. bianchii	Bianchi's
P.c. chrysomelas	Khivan
P.c. zerafschanicus	Zerafshan
P.c. shawi	Yarkand

(c) The *mongolicus* group — similar to the white-wings but the general plumage tends to coppery-maroon with green reflections. The neck collar is wide and pronounced.

P.c. turcestanicus	Syr Daria
P.c. mongolicus	Kirghiz

(d) The Tarim pheasant — *P.c. tarimensis*, the olive-rumped pheasant, is intermediate between the preceding western forms and the remaining eastern subspecies.

(e) The *torquatus* group — this includes the remaining pheasants of the eastern half of Asia, known as the grey-rumped pheasants.

P.c. hagenbecki	Kobdo ring-necked
P.c. pallasi	Manchurian ring-necked
P.c. karpowi	Korean ring-necked
P.c. kiangsuensis	Shansi
P.c. alaschanicus	Alashan
P.c. edzinensis	Gobi ring-necked
P.c. satscheuensis	Satchu ring-necked
P.c. vlangalli	Zaidan
P.c. strauchi	Strauch's
P.c. sohokhotensis	Sohokhoto
P.c. suehschanenis	Sungpan
P.c. elegans	Stone's
P.c. rothschildi	Rothschild's
P.c. decollatus	Kweichow
P.c. takatsukasae	Tonkinese ring-necked
P.c. torquatus	Chinese ring-necked
P.c. formosanus	Taiwan ring-necked

There are also two subspecies of the Japanese green pheasant.

This species only differs from *P. colchicus* in the plumage of the male which is predominantly green with a purplish tinge.

P.v. versicolor	Southern green
P.v. robustipes	Northern green

More detailed descriptions of each subspecies and their plumages are available in Delacour (1977) and Johnsgard (1986).

INTRODUCTIONS OF THE PHEASANT OUTSIDE ITS NATIVE RANGE

The natural range of the pheasant has been greatly extended due to introductions by man. Along with chukar and grey partridges, starlings and house sparrows, the pheasant has one of the widest introduced distributions of any bird.

Long (1981) records attempts to introduce this species into nearly 50 countries including some on every continent except Antarctica. The natural range has been successfully extended to include the temperate regions of Europe and North America, the Hawaiian islands (introduced 1865), New Zealand, Chile (1886), St Helena, King Island, Rottnest Island and Tasmania. There are unconfirmed reports of successful introductions to Eleuthera in the Bahamas, Flinders Island in Australia and on the South Australian mainland. Initial successes were reported following releases in the Dominican Republic, Panama (1959), Pitcairn Island and Taiwan (1935), but these have subsequently failed. Unsuccessful attempts at introduction have also been made in Madeira, Cyprus, Alaska, Bermuda, Peru (1970), Tahiti (1938), Mauritius, Kangaroo Island and other areas on mainland Australia (Meinertzhagen 1912, Guild 1938, Hachisuka and Udagawa 1951, Bourne 1957, Williams 1960, Wetmore 1965).

The earliest recorded introduction comes from mythology. Legend has it that the first pheasants to reach Europe arrived in Greece in 1300 BC aboard the *Argo* following Jason's search for the Golden Fleece. These first pheasants are said to have been brought from the valley of the River Phasis in the Colchis region of the Caucasus, which is now the Soviet Republic of Georgia. These early origins of the European pheasants are immortalised in the pheasant's scientific name, *Phasianus colchicus*.

Britain

There is a widely held belief that the pheasant was introduced to Britain by the Romans. These people were certainly familiar with the bird. Although there is some evidence of pheasants in this country in early times — for instance, pictures incorporated into 4th century Romano-British mosaic pavements (Rainey 1973) — these are by no means conclusive. Yapp (1983) believes that they are either copies incorporated directly from Rome or they have been misidentified. This author states that the earliest certain pictures of pheasants are to be found in the Sherborne Missal, dated between 1396 and 1407, and that it would be unwise to conclude that this species was well known or feral before the 14th century. They were probably brought over by the Normans. Certainly they were breeding in the wild during the late 15th century, when they gained some degree of legal protection from the crown (Lever 1977). Their range spread to Ireland and Scotland in the late 16th century (O'Gorman 1970) and Wales in the 17th (Matheson 1963). However, they did not spread across the entire country until the late 18th century or become a prominent part of the game bag until the 19th.

The original introduction to Britain was *P.c. colchicus*, known as the English or black-necked pheasant. Further races were introduced later, Chinese ring-necks (*P.c. torquatus*) around 1768; green pheasants (*P. versicolor*) from Japan in 1840; Mongolians (*P.c. mongolicus*) in 1898–1900; Prince of Wales pheasants (*P.c. principalis*) in 1902; and at least two other races, *P.c. pallasi* and *P.c. satscheuensis*, were imported early this century (Koch 1956). These races have all subsequently interbred and the British population is now a conglomerate of many different characters.

Europe

As described previously the pheasant was a popular bird with the Romans. Evidence from written accounts of recipes and rearing methods suggests that they kept them as a favoured table bird, reared like domestic fowl. It was the Romans who were considered to have introduced them to Italy, Germany and France (Lowe 1933).

In more recent times this range has been further extended. Pheasants were first released in Norway in 1875–1876 near Oslo. Following further introductions they are now established in the cultivated areas in Ostfold, Akershus and Vestfold (Myrberget 1976).

In Finland, pheasants were raised and released near Helsinki at the turn of the century and from these birds and from other continuing releases the population had built up to 20 000 birds in 1958 (Merikallio 1958).

In the USSR introductions and reacclimatisations have been attempted in a number of areas. They have been established in Transcaucasia since 1890 and reintroduced to the northern Caucasus since 1930. Other attempts at introductions in Moldavia, RSFSR, West Siberia, the Ukraine and near Odessa and Moscow have all met with failure (Nazerenko and Gurskii 1963, Yanushevich 1966).

The range of the pheasant in Europe is thus wholly due to introductions by man. This range covers almost all the temperate regions stretching from Britain, Ireland, Southern Norway, Sweden and Finland in the north to Spain, Italy, Yugoslavia, Greece and Bulgaria in the south.

North America

The earliest recorded attempt at introduction on this continent was the release of six pairs by the governor of New York in 1730, although these failed to become established (Silverstein and Silverstein 1974). Further abortive attempts occurred in New York in 1733, New Jersey in 1790 (Allen, 1962), California in the 1870s and 1880s and Oregon in 1881.

The first successful introduction occurred in 1882 when Judge O.N. Denny, then American Consul General in Shanghai, China, sent 30 ring-necked pheasants to Oregon. Of these, 26 survived and were liberated in the Williamette Valley, Oregon, supplemented by further releases two years later (Shaw 1908). Following this initial success, further releases occurred in Washington in 1883, Colorado in 1885, New York between 1886 and 1891, New Jersey in 1887, Georgia in 1888, California in 1889, Illinois in the 1890s, Pennsylvania between 1892 and 1895, Wisconsin between 1892, and the turn of the century, Montana prior to 1895,

Massachusetts in 1897 or 1898 and Ohio, Utah, Michigan, Indiana and Minnesota around 1900 (Phillips 1928, Bump 1941, 1968, Allen 1962, Ellis and Anderson 1963, Sandfort 1963, Townsend 1963, Janson *et al.* 1971).

After these initial releases the pheasant spread to cover most of its current range by the 1920s and 1930s, assisted in many cases by state-sponsored releasing programmes.

Initial introductions used stocks from England and China (*P.c. colchicus* and *torquatus* respectively). Subsequently other sub-species have been used, often in attempts to increase success following early failures. Thus *P.c. mongolicus* was used in California in 1894, Japanese green pheasants (*P. versicolor*) in 1885 (Gottschalk 1967) and 1960 in Virginia (Tuttle 1963), and Bianchi's white wings (*P. bianchii*) in Nevada and New Mexico in the 1960s (Christensen 1963, 1967, Bump 1968). Korean birds were tried in New York in 1968 (Colson 1968), similarly with Persian and Talisch Caucasian black-necks (*P.c. persicus* and *P.c. talischensis*) in South Carolina, Kentucky, Virginia and Florida in the 1960s (Nelson 1963, Robinson 1969). Crosses of these black-necks with ring-necks have been used in Florida, Missouri, Virginia, Alabama, Arkansas, South Carolina, Kentucky and Maryland since 1956 (Long 1981).

Attempts have been made to introduce pheasants into Alaska since 1934, but with no apparent success (Gabrielson and Lincoln 1959).

Unsuccessful attempts were made to introduce this species into British Columbia in Canada in 1882 (Carl and Guiguet 1958), Nova Scotia in the 1890s and parts of Quebec (Phillips 1928). In 1910 the propagation of pheasants was taken over by the Game Commission who annually released large numbers in many areas until 1954. These activities have established pheasants in the most southern parts of Canada: New Brunswick, Nova Scotia and the southern regions of Quebec, Ontario, Manitoba, Saskatchewan, Alberta and British Columbia (Godfrey 1966).

Australia and New Zealand

The pheasant was first introduced to Australia by the Victoria Zoological and Acclimatisation Society in 1864, but failed, unlike that other famous introduction, the rabbit. Various releases

occurred in Victoria and Tasmania in the 19th century, but without success. In 1961, pheasants were again introduced onto the
mainland in South Australia amid widespread protests, the attitudes
of the antipodeans to introducing non-native species having
changed dramatically by this time. Long (1981) also reports the
introduction of a single pheasant, sex unspecified but presumably
a hen, onto Kangaroo Island in 1969, although the success of this
unusual approach has not been recorded.

Pheasants can now be found on Rottnest Island, King Island
and in Tasmania, introductions to the Australian mainland not
having met with any success.

Introductions to New Zealand began in 1842 and the birds were
successfully established by 1845 (Thomson 1922). Large-scale
rearing has subsequently spread this species to all suitable areas
on the North and South Islands (Westerskov 1962).

2 Study Areas and Techniques

Throughout this book we shall draw not only on our own research experiences in Britain, but on information collected over many years across the world, largely within the pheasant's introduced range. Much of our information comes from the cornbelt of the United States and we aim to point to similarities and differences in pheasant ecology between the continents. The pheasant has been least studied in its native lands, primarily because of the lack of interest in it as a sporting bird in these areas. In western countries the study of their ecology has been important in enabling man to manage them efficiently, increase breeding populations, raise productivity and generate larger populations for shooting. For the most part however, we describe research findings based on four distinct study areas – Damerham in Hampshire, Fulwell in Oxfordshire, North Farm in Sussex, and Lyons Estate in Co. Kildare, Ireland.

STUDY AREAS

Damerham

In the late 1940s to the mid-1960s the large Damerham Estate was used by the ICI Game Research Station (which later developed into the Game Conservancy) as the main grey partridge and pheasant study area. Later the estate changed the shooting tenancy, farms became larger and although interest in game continued it ceased to be a major study site. In 1979 part of the area, known as Knoll Farm, comprising 220 ha of arable lowland over chalk, was surveyed for use as a study site for the new Pheasant Project set up at the Fordingbridge headquarters of the Game Conservancy. More than 70% of the area is given over to growing arable crops in which winter barley, winter wheat, spring barley and ryegrass predominate. Almost 12% of the area is afforested, largely with native broadleaves and mixtures of fir, cypress, Scots pine, beech, silver birch, sycamore, and cherry. Fields are separated by hedges containing the usual species of shrubs characteristic of chalk including spindle, although hawthorn predominates. Nettles, willowherb, bramble, cow parsley and various grasses dominate the hedge bottoms and the occasional ditch.

The older blocks of woodland and shelterbelts comprising beech are particularly windswept places during the winter months, lacking any significant shrub or ground cover. The younger conifer plantations do, however, provide some cover to pheasants during the worst weather conditions. The relatively large fields, being on average about 25 ha, give a barren appearance and little by way of game lives out in the centre of these blocks until the new corn begins to flourish.

Lyons Estate

Lyons Estate straddles the borders of countries Kildare and Dublin and was purchased by University College Dublin in 1962 for use as an experimental farm. The area used comprised 464 ha lying between 60 m and 200 m above sea-level, mainly flat but rising in one corner to form Lyons Hill. The low lying areas are intensively cultivated on a six-year rotation with grass being the main break crop. Higher ground tends to be permanent pasture. Other habitats comprise some 62 ha of scrub and woodland and approximately 14 km of hedgerow. For cropping purposes the average field size was 4.5 ha, but due to insubstantial field boundaries the average area of open ground was about 30 ha. Prior to its purchase by the University, the estate was run as a large driven pheasant shoot and the woodland areas were managed for game. This is no longer the case and large areas previously occupied by woods, scrub and parkland have been reclaimed to facilitate intensive agriculture. The remaining areas of woodland are currently unmanaged and subject to progressive clearance at the rate of about 1 ha per year.

Fulwell

The Fulwell estate in Oxfordshire was used by Matt Ridley whilst undertaking his doctorate research on the mating system of the pheasant at the Edward Grey Institute of Field Ornithology, University of Oxford. His study described the behaviour of the sexes throughout the year, upon which we were able to build by studying birds at Damerham. His study area comprised 150 ha of arable farmland surrounding four woods. The ground is undulating at about 150 m above sea-level, with well-drained calcareous soil.

There are essentially six habitat types on the area. Open fields sown with similar crops to those at Damerham represent about 75% of the total area of the farm. There are about 2 ha of hedgerows, again comprising similar species to those at Damerham and about 16 ha of mixed woodland, largely mixed plantations of fir, cypress, cherry, beech and sycamore. The plantations were planted some thirty years ago (in the late 1950s) and form, in their young stages, thickets of about 8–10 m in height, with little understorey or ground flora. There is approximately 6 ha of mature deciduous woodland, largely consisting of mixed beech and ash plantations, elder and bramble. This woodland has an abundant ground flora of nettles, cow parsley (at the edges) and grasses. Scrub and immature plantations comprise almost 6 ha of the total, being less than 15 years of age, together with older hawthorn scrub habitat. As at Damerham a number of the woodlands, particularly the larger areas, have rides and clearings which are prime habitats for pheasants during the winter and also for the establishment of breeding territories.

Sussex Downs

These downs in West Sussex were the main study area of the Game Conservancy's partridge studies carried out by Dr G.R. Potts and colleagues, concentrating on one area, North Farm. The area is freely-drained, open downland under arable agriculture with fields averaging 16 ha, though with half being over 20 ha in size. The soil is mostly a chalk rendzina with flints and until the mid-1960s farming consisted largely of a rotation of spring-sown barley with undersown clover leys. Cereals constitute about 60% of the total land area, with few woods, but a number of hedges similar to those found at Damerham and Fulwell.

During his studies Dick Potts plotted the positions of pheasant broods together with the number of adults and young within a brood. In this book we use his data in order to relate brood size, from which we derive chick survival rate, to insect food supplies in cereal fields on a between-year basis. Potts and his co-workers sampled populations of invertebrate food items available to grey partridge and pheasant chicks at North Farm over the period 1970 to the present time. By kind permission we also present these data in the book.

METHODS

The wide range of studies of the pheasant have all used their own particular methods. However, some general methods are common to a number of studies and are described here, while more specialised techniques are introduced in the relevant sections of the text.

Trapping and marking pheasants

In order to follow the histories and fates of our study populations we needed to be able to catch birds at particular times of the year and fit them with a marker allowing each individual to be recognised at a distance. Pheasants are quite easy to catch, particularly during the winter and early spring when they can be attracted into weldmesh funnel traps baited with grain. In the late spring and early summer it becomes more difficult to catch them, largely because their diet has, by this time, changed to young shoots.

Each bird was marked with a coloured fin-tab bearing a black number and letter on each side. The fin-tab was made of durable plastic and stands upright on the back of the bird so that the letter or number can be read through a telescope up to a distance of about 100 m (Fig. 2.1).

In the late summer some of our study estates released hand-reared poults in order to increase numbers available for the shooting season. So as to determine the origin of birds in the following winter and spring we made sure that all released poults carried small numbered aluminium wing-tags. These were fitted

Fig. 2.1 The construction and positioning of back tags used in this study.

to the small flap of skin on the wing called the patagium. The lack of nerve endings in the patagium means that the birds wearing these tags feel no discomfort.

Determining a bird's age

In order to distinguish between first-winter birds (immatures) and adults we measured the size of the proximal primary wing feather. We used the widest diameter of the shaft at the point of the scar (Fig. 2.2) using two rulers mounted on a board and with a tapering aperture of from 4.5 to 2 mm width over a length of 100 mm. We had to calibrate this technique with feathers from birds of known age. On Damerham we found that female shaft diameters varied between 2.18 and 3.6 mm, males between 2.16 and 4.32 mm, but that by using a value of 3.2 mm the males could be separated into adults and immatures with 95% accuracy. The technique has been satisfactorily tested by other workers (see Greenberg, Etter and Anderson 1972). Matt Ridley, in his studies, found that females were difficult to age and he divided hens into two distinct categories − adults with a shaft diameter greater than 3.1 mm, and immatures in which shaft diameters were less than 2.7 mm. However, 27% of all hens had shaft diameters between 2.7 mm and 3.1 mm and so unfortunately could not be aged using this method. In Ireland, a measure of 3.1 mm separated adult and juvenile cocks while adult hens were over 3.1 mm with juveniles below 2.8 mm. In this study 17% of hens could not be aged (Robertson 1985a).

Censusing breeding birds

A number of techniques have been used to estimate breeding population size. Marking the position of crowing cocks on a map is one. Another is mapping all individuals of both sexes and then calculating an index with which to adjust the number of hens since they are cryptically plumaged and are more difficult to see than cocks. In our studies we favoured the latter approach largely because we were dealing with relatively dense populations over small areas and most of our birds were individually marked.

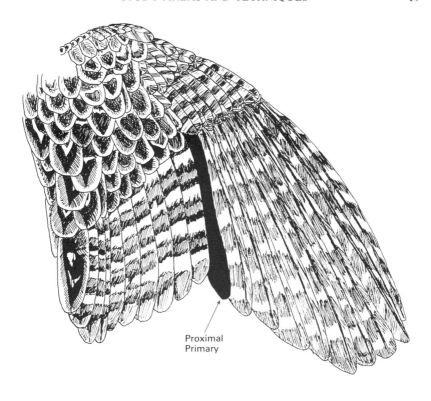

Fig. 2.2 The position of the proximal primary feather and the measurement of shaft diameter.

Pheasants are most active for about two hours at dawn and two hours at dusk. During the period October to April vegetation cover is quite sparse and we were able to observe birds emerging from the woodland edges to feed on adjacent fields. Birds were observed from a vehicle to reduce disturbance and their location and identity were marked on a large-scale map.

During the winter, and during harem formation, pheasants are gregarious. We defined a group of pheasants as all individuals within 5 m of each other. In cases where densities of birds are low, problems in defining a group rarely occur.

Territory mapping is an important tool for determining the number of territorial males. Male territories are mapped by plotting the positions of fights and other boundary disputes, the daily ranges of territorial males on open fields and the positions of crowing males in cover. Polygons are drawn by joining the outermost records of each male when acting in a territorial manner. Although this 'convex polygon' method has disadvantages for determining the cores of activity of individual birds when compared to methods based on the probability of certain areas being used (such as defined by Dixon and Chapman 1980), we considered it to be the only practicable method of measuring as many male home ranges as possible during the period when males were still readily seen in the open.

Measuring nest success

Nest success is one of the most important and widely studied aspects of pheasant ecology. Apart from reviewing previous work

Plate 1. A scene from the Knoll Farm study area in Hampshire. (*D.A. Hill*)

we also examined a large store of British nest record data collected from a number of different sources. Our first set of data was that collected by amateur ornithologists for the British Trust for Ornithology's (BTO) Nest Record Scheme. This records 1650 nests found throughout Britain between 1950 and 1985. A second set of 522 nest records was collected by the Game Conservancy from keepered estates in their Pheasant Nest Recording Scheme (PNRS) during 1978 and 1979. These records tended to be more detailed than those collected by the BTO scheme and are used to examine individual causes of loss. Lastly, we also collected data on nest success during the course of radiotracking hen pheasants during the summer. This provides the most detailed data, but only for 58 nests.

Rates of nest survival and hence success were calculated using the methods suggested by Mayfield (1961, 1975) as presented by Hensler and Nichols (1981). These estimate survival from the number of days during which nests were under observation and the number of losses occurring during each period.

Eggs were assumed to have been laid at an average rate of one per 1.4 days and incubation (beginning with the laying of the last egg and ending with hatching) to last 25 days (taken from Cramp and Simmons 1980).

Estimating chick survival

Pheasant broods have been counted on annual partridge brood surveys by G.R. Potts and his co-workers on the 6200 ha South Downs study area in West Sussex. Potts and his team also sampled invertebrates living within cereal fields on the study area during the first week in June in the period 1970 to the present time. We have used these data in order to look at the relationship between changes in invertebrate numbers in different years and the survival rate of chicks. An average brood size at fledging of 9.83 would indicate that 100% of the brood had survived to that time since 9.83 is the average clutch size of the pheasant after accounting for infertile eggs (see Chapter 5). By counting brood sizes seen on cereal fields in mid to late August it is possible to calculate the survival rate of chicks in any given year.

Plate II. Dr G.R. Potts and a view of the study area on the Sussex Downs. (*The Game Conservancy*)

The National Game Census

Repeated use is made of data on numbers of game and predators shot per year in Britain. These data have been collected in a systematic manner by the Game Conservancy's National Game Census since 1961 although other, less comparable, data stretch back to the early 19th century. The National Game Census (NGC) annually collects data from approximately 600 estates covering some 800 000 ha of land. These data include the numbers of each species of game shot, the numbers reared and the return rates from shooting of reared birds if they were tagged. The scheme also collects data on the numbers of predators killed and records details of the size of the estate and areas of woodland, along with the numbers of gamekeepers. This wealth of information can be used to examine changes in the numbers of each species killed or reared per unit area since 1961 and this is thought to reflect changes in their populations with some degree of accuracy. However, these data only refer to shooting estates and cannot easily be extrapolated to the status of animals outside these areas or to national populations. Nevertheless it does provide an invaluable method of monitoring changes in our more common species.

Radiotracking

The methods of marking that we have described above have advantages in that they are cheap to produce and easy to attach. However, once the vegetation has grown up, birds become almost impossible to see. Furthermore, it is not possible with such markers to obtain an unbiased assessment of the bird's use of its habitat. For this reason we used radiotelemetry. This technique involves attaching small radiotransmitters to the birds. These then emit a signal detectable by a hand-held receiver and antenna.

We used radiotelemetry in our studies for two main reasons. The first was to be able to follow the female back to her nest to determine clutch success and to follow the fate of her brood.

Plate III. Small radiotransmitters were attached to the birds which enabled their movements to be accurately followed. (*D.A. Hill*)

Secondly, radiotelemetry enabled us to measure home range sizes and investigate the preferences for different habitats during the course of the year.

Radiotransmitters used were either 12 g in weight (one-stage with shorter ground to ground range) or 18 g designs (two-stage with longer ground to ground range) mounted using either a 'rucksack' type wing loop harness on the back of the bird or neck collars (Kenward 1987). We located birds between one and three times daily and plotted positions on a large-scale map. The data were then fed into a computer using map coordinates. Home range sizes were calculated from thirty points, three locations per day for ten consecutive days (Hill and Robertson 1987a). On average we were able to detect birds at distances of 1.5 km, although this varied depending on individual transmitters and the terrain in which the bird lived. Signal strength attenuates sharply, for example, in woodland.

Throughout this book we have tried to present the statistical analyses of data as clearly as possible without compromising the flow of the text. Significance is stated at the 5% level, and, where applicable, average values are followed by one standard error. At the 5% level of significance there is a 20:1 chance that the observed difference is simply a random event rather than a real difference.

3 During the Winter

The winter places many constraints on pheasants: fields provide them with little food or cover, the days become short with long nights, while sub-zero conditions are common. How does this species cope with the strictures of the winter and how has it adapted to survive during this period?

The choice of habitat is a key aspect in the ecology and survival of pheasants during the winter, and most of the management of wild pheasants aims to provide them with food and cover at this time of year. Only recently have we begun to understand their social system, one feature of which is the general segregation of the sexes into separate groups. This in itself is important if we are to understand differences in habitat selection between the sexes.

We begin our investigations at the end of the summer when broods of young accompanied by hens, and the more solitary males, begin to lay down reserves of fat to take them through the winter. We then move on to explain the changes which take place in their social structure and habitat preferences as they enter the winter period.

FAMILY GROUPS

After the fields of wheat and barley have been cut, broods of pheasants can often be seen and counted at the field edge, feeding on the spoils of the harvest. Still in family groups and accompanied by the female parent, they usually remain like this until late October and early November. There has been little work on the social structure at the end of autumn, but studies on other galliformes, notably grey and red-legged partridge, have shown that winter coveys are made up of family members and relatives. Pheasants do not form coveys in this sense although broods are often joined by males at the end of the harvest.

Young pheasants are considered to be dependent on the female for about 75 days (Hiatt and Fisher 1974) although we have observed females separating from broods at about 60 days. Interestingly, covey forming tends to occur in ground-dwelling bird species which feed in the open throughout the year. Grey and red-legged partridge are essentially open habitat species and rely on vigilance to detect predators. Pheasants on the other hand retire to cover during the day, emerging to feed in the first and last few hours of daylight, so that for most of the day it is cover rather than vigilance that affords them protection. This diurnal pattern of feeding has been shown quite clearly in a study in the United States (Dalke 1937). In this study, very few birds were seen feeding in the open in the middle of the day and at that time their crops were often less than 5% full, suggesting that they do not feed much whilst in cover (Fig. 3.1).

When pheasants do feed in the open they generally do so in small groups, and it is probable that the family group stays together for much of the winter, although there is as yet rather little firm evidence to support this. We know much more about their social behaviour later in the year.

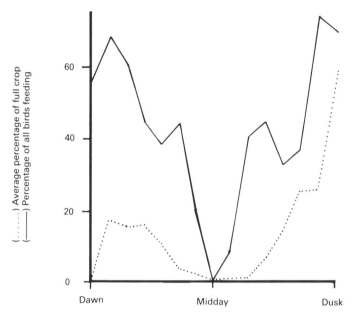

Fig. 3.1 Diurnal feeding activity (solid line) and the amount of food in the crop (dotted line). (Redrawn from Dalke 1937.)

DIET, WEIGHT AND STARVATION

Pheasants are generally omnivorous during winter, eating grain, seeds, berries and other fruits, green shoots, small arthropods, molluscs and occasionally small vertebrates. Their diet is most diverse of all during autumn. Dalke (1937) recorded 106 species of seeds and fruit in the gut of birds caught in October. When snow covers the ground, pheasants will also dig down to obtain food. Acorns are an important source of food in many localities, and hazel nuts are also eaten whole. Fruits of apple, raspberry, blackberry, hawthorn and blackthorn are eaten in autumn and early winter, as well as roots, bulbs, rhizomes, and tubers of the *Solanaceae* and *Compositae*.

Collections and analyses of crop contents throughout the year have shown that for birds sampled from woods, parks and pasture where they find their own food without help from man, grain represents between 0 and 3.5% by volume of the diet, with about 30% by volume in January attributed to animal food. Earthworms often constitute the major animal food item in winter months, and can represent as much as 11.5% of the diet by volume in November (Collinge 1924–27).

The Game Conservancy conducted a wild pheasant study on the population of pheasants inhabiting Brownsea Island in Poole Harbour, Dorset, England, in the early 1970s. Part of this project involved a study of pheasant diet through faecal analysis supported by observations of feeding birds.

On this island, tree fruits (particularly acorns) were favoured, with a transition to roots of grass and sorrel (mainly *Rumex acetosella*) by December (Lachlan and Bray 1973). The birds usually fed on grassland and grass leaves and stems were the most important food items eaten in winter (Fig. 3.2). In this study insects were also widely eaten in the autumn, representing 20% of the total diet by volume in August and September when many wood ants were eaten, and 15% in October when the insects were mainly beetles. The dominance of cultivated grain in winter

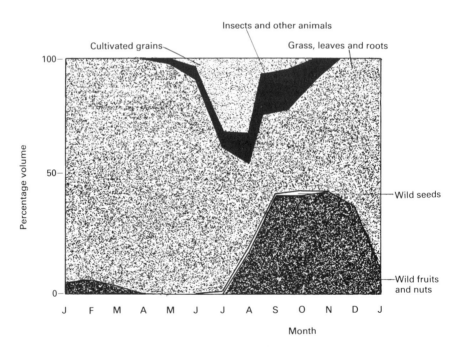

Fig. 3.2 Seasonal changes in the percentage by volume of different food items found in faeces of pheasants from Brownsea Island, England. (Redrawn from Lachlan and Bray 1973.)

and wild seeds and fruit in autumn has also been shown by an early study in Michigan (Fig. 3.3).

Grass and clover leaves are often favoured winter food items. In a Danish study these items were found to be present in 50–90% of crops during November–February with roots also well represented (Hammer *et al.* 1958). In a Finnish study 11 crops analysed during December–March contained, in terms of dry weight, 81.8% wheat, 7.8% maize, 8.6% fat hen, 1.3% barley, and 0.2% hemp nettle (Pulliainen 1966).

The foods eaten follow a definite seasonal trend in most areas. Generally grain and seeds are eaten in early winter, followed by roots and tubers later on, with insects predominating in spring and summer. A study near the Black Sea found 45 species of invertebrates in the summer diet while in the Zeravshan Valley (USSR) pheasants were reputed to have cleared cotton fields of locusts (Dementiev and Gladkov 1967). By contrast a Yugoslavian

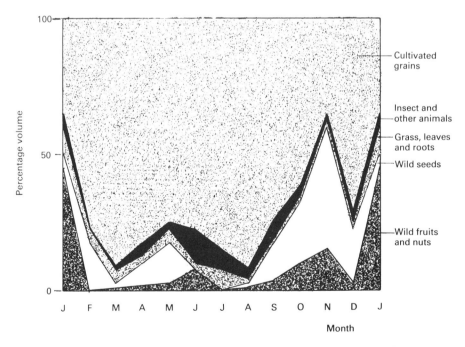

Fig. 3.3 Seasonal changes in the percentage by volume of different food items found in crops and gizzards from pheasants in the United States. (Redrawn from Dalke 1937.)

study revealed that of 201 crops analysed 55% by volume contained plant material in May–June, compared with 95% in December–April (Pekic 1962).

The provision of 'artificial' food such as cereals and, to a lesser extent, pellets in feeding hoppers, together with the planting of seed-producing game-crops, doubtless have important effects on the condition of pheasants during the winter. These techniques are generally practised on keepered estates or on those which rear and release pheasants. Wild-bred pheasants often do not receive the same treatment, generally because they tend to live at lower densities than those created by hand-rearing.

In the United States unusually heavy snowfall in some years often leads to widespread mortality through starvation and chilling. In cases where snow covers the ground from the beginning of November to the end of March, starvation in the later months is commonplace. During such times they are also more vulnerable to predation and have been observed to collapse under stress. In one study (Nelson and Janson 1949) it was found that cocks that had died of starvation were only 53% of the weight of healthy males, while in hens the weight difference was 60%. The sex ratio of dead birds was heavily biased towards hens, suggesting that starvation affects them sooner than it does cocks. Under experimental conditions, however, Latham (1947) observed the opposite. Furthermore Tester and Olson (1959) found no significant difference in the survival time of penned male and female pheasants given no access to food. Most of them succumbed after about 16 days of starvation under average maximum and minimum temperatures of −4°C and −15°C. However, such unpleasant experiments tell us very little about the survival of birds in truly wild environments.

In cold weather when energy loss is high, pheasants appear adapted to a 'negative energy balance' (Gates and Hale 1974). In Finland during extreme cold, pheasants may not feed at all, but attempt to conserve energy by remaining still and torpid for days at a time (Lehtonen 1975). During a week of extreme cold in December 1981 many of the pheasants studied by Ridley at Fulwell stayed in trees throughout the day and apparently did not attempt to feed. They appear to be quite tolerant of all but the most extreme conditions and are quite able to sit out the usual cold snaps of British winters.

Plate IV. Male pheasants roosting in a tree during the winter. (*John Marchington*)

This policy of 'sit and wait' cannot cope with longer or more intense cold and in these circumstances the birds must start to search for food. Crops of starving birds are, as one might expect, generally empty, and intestinal bleeding, as a result of coarse material passing through the digestive tract, can take place in extreme cases. In very cold conditions some pheasants have been found with the flesh and feathers of other pheasants in their crops and gizzards, indicating that they had supplemented their diets by feeding on carrion. Thankfully, the conditions leading to such deprivations are uncommon and pheasants are less affected by winter conditions than many other, smaller birds.

In some years, certain tree species produce fruit which are readily eaten by pheasants. Oak and beech, which crop very erratically and produce highly variable amounts of acorns and beech mast respectively, are two notable examples. At Knoll Farm, we have been monitoring winter weight by catching hens during late January–March; 1984 was a 'mast' year and vast quantities of both beech nuts and acorns issued from trees with the approach of winter. In the following late winter months, female pheasants were heavier by an average of 70 g compared to years when mast and acorn supplies were low. While we have not monitored mast and acorn availability it seems that, since these are readily taken food items, they contributed to the heavier weights shown by hens in the winter of 1984/85.

In contrast to the vagaries of natural foods, artificially supplied foods are predictable from year to year. Gamekeepers provide extra feed in hoppers or by scattering it along strawed rides in woodland. Winter feeding doubtless improves pheasant densities and condition. Even so, for reasons we shall argue later, it is probably unlikely that winter condition plays an important part in egg production, quality or hatchability (Gates and Woehler 1968), especially in Britain where weather conditions are generally less severe than, for example, the northern parts of the United States. It appears more likely to cause earlier laying, given that spring weather conditions are favourable.

SEGREGATION OF THE SEXES

In Britain, winter flocks of pheasants tend to be largely of birds of the same sex. However, whether pheasants segregate into groups of the same sex during winter appears to depend largely on the amount and distribution of habitat available to them. In the cornbelt of the United States sexual segregation in autumn—early winter is much less prevalent (Robertson 1958, Gates and Hale 1974) than on farmland in Britain. This probably reflects the scarcity of permanent cover in those parts of the States and the concentration of birds within what cover there is. Sexual segregation also occurs less when birds live at a low density. In the Irish study (Robertson 1986), the extent of sexual segregation was reduced in autumn and early winter and none was apparent in late winter due largely to small average flock sizes and a large number of solitary birds. These studies of populations at low densities or in areas with little cover are in contrast to those observed by Hill and Ridley (1987) in which the sexes were very much segregated during the early winter (Table 3.1). In these examples the expected proportion of groups seen to contain only individuals of one sex is calculated on the basis of average flock size and sex ratio. Table 3.2 shows that in autumn—early winter

Table 3.1 Segregation by sex of pheasant groups from autumn to spring on the Damerham, Fulwell and Lyons study areas (test of equality of two proportions * P<0.001)

		Proportion of groups of one sex	
	Number of groups	Observed	Expected
Damerham, England			
Autumn−early winter	49	0.660	0.283*
Late winter	52	0.558	0.075*
Fulwell, England			
Autumn−early winter	353	0.494	0.247*
Late winter	586	0.589	0.269*
Lyons, Ireland			
Autumn−early winter	253	0.814	0.567*
Late winter	151	0.855	0.823

and late winter periods at both Damerham and Fulwell, a greater proportion of groups contained only one sex than would have been expected based on the sex ratio and average size of flock.

Living in groups is thought, for female pheasants, to be advantageous both in enabling them to find food more easily and in looking out for predators. Males on the other hand tend to remain relatively solitary, sometimes forming all-male groups, but these are smaller than female flocks. Mixed sex flocks do occur but they are not especially common. The observed sex ratio and flock structure can also be influenced by sexual differences in habitat use and the response to management. In early winter the sex ratio of birds feeding in open fields significantly favours males as females move back into permanent cover in response both to the provision of food by gamekeepers, and to shelter (Fig. 3.4).

GROUP SIZE AND STRUCTURE

The gregarious habits of pheasants at this time of the year have not been studied in detail, although our work at Damerham and Matt Ridley's at Fulwell have highlighted certain changes as the winter progresses. From October to March 97−100% of females and 46−86% of males at Fulwell, and 93−98% of females and 59−71% of males at Damerham were in groups of two or more

Table 3.2 The composition of all pheasant groups seen on the two areas (Damerham in parentheses) in late autumn, winter and spring

Period:	Autumn			Winter			Spring	
Dates:	17/10–10/11	11/11–6/12	22/11–29/11	24/1–28/3	1/3–26/3	12/3–26/3	27/3–10/4	28/3–11/5
Total no. groups watched	169	184	(49)	86	500	(52)	336	(87)
Mean group sizes								
All groups	4.02	2.17	(3.33)	3.14	3.87	(5.10)	2.72	(3.83)
All-male groups	1.78	1.72	(2.52)	1.46	1.46	(3.07)	1.14	(2.5)
All-female groups	3.88	3.20	(3.25)	7.05	6.16	(4.92)	4.17	(2.0)
Mixed groups	8.88	4.08	(4.93)	5.90	8.89	(4.31)	5.02	(3.07)
Males per mixed group	3.54	1.86	(2.00)	2.09	1.96	(1.27)	1.08	(1.05)
Females per mixed group	5.33	2.21	(2.93)	3.81	6.81	(3.04)	3.93	(2.02)
Proportion (%) of:								
Males in all-male group	47	85	(50)	31	22	(39)	23	(3)
Females in all-female group	20	56	(38)	45	35	(38)	33	(2)
Solitary males	14	31	(29)	36	35	(32)	54	(41)
Solitary females	1	3	(2)	0	1	(7)	3	(2)

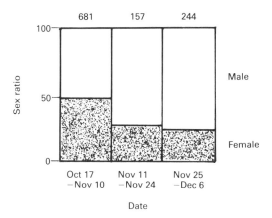

Fig. 3.4 Changes in the sex ratio of pheasants seen feeding on ploughed fields between October and December at Fulwell, England. (Redrawn from Hill and Ridley 1987.)

birds (Table 3.2). At both sites female groups were larger than male groups and the number of males in mixed groups declined similarly through the winter to early spring. The proportion of males in all-male groups and the proportion of females in all-female groups declined from winter to early spring and the number of lone males increased. This, of course, is associated with the increase in the male's territorial aggressiveness, such that they become mutually intolerant of each other as the breeding season approaches. We shall be discussing territoriality in the next chapter.

Males do not appear to form regular associations with other males before the breeding season and certainly not during it in the case of territorial individuals. Males at Fulwell have been seen to join and leave groups of other birds during the winter more often than have females, so they are much less likely than females to form consistent long-term associations with other individuals.

Females on the other hand are much more gregarious. However, they can be divided into two types, those which do form regular associations with other individuals, which we call 'flock members', and those which 'drift' between different flocks on successive days through the winter, which we appropriately call 'drifters'. At Fulwell, females bearing numbered back-mounted fin-tabs were watched at dawn as they emerged from the woods to feed. They were categorised as flock members or drifters on the basis of whether they were regularly seen in the same flock. This enabled the identity of the drifter females to be ascertained. At Fulwell drifter females were predominantly immature birds whereas flock members were adults (Table 3.3) (Ridley 1983).

So in habitats which provide adequate cover, pheasants form relatively large all-female groups, while males tend to be solitary or to form small groups. Female groups generally contain older females which are usually consistent members of the same flock together with first-winter drifter females which move between a number of different flocks.

WINTER HABITAT SELECTION

Gamekeepers often talk of some woods being good for hens, and others being preferred by cocks, and there appears to be some truth in this (Cheng 1964). That pheasants exhibit sexual segregation in winter also suggests that the two sexes might differ in their selection of and preference for different habitats at this time of year.

In order to find out which habitats were preferred by each sex, we visited a number of estates on shooting days and, standing behind the guns, counted the numbers of birds being pushed from cover. We separated counts into cocks and hens and split the results into four different types of pheasant drive: woodland, game crops, hedges and a mixture of game crops and hedges.

The next step was to divide the numbers of each sex seen on each drive by the area of the drive to arrive at a density estimate. This was then converted to a relative density estimate by expressing it as a proportion of the total number of pheasants seen on that day. This not only corrected for differences in population

Table 3.3 The age of flock and 'drifter' females at Fulwell

	Immature	Adult	Unknown
Drifter	9	4	4
Flock member	9	28	9

sizes between estates but also for the fact that absolute numbers of birds declined through the winter as a result of mortality and dispersal. Comparison of the relative density estimates between different habitats from all estates combined therefore allows us to find whether different types of habitat are preferred by each sex.

Relative density estimates for the four broad habitat categories are shown in Table 3.4. Hedgerow drives contained much higher densities of males than females. This is an interesting finding and may relate to some males, through their mutual intolerance of one another and much smaller group sizes when compared to females, being forced to live in 'sub-optimal' hedgerow habitats. Our results may indicate more of the younger subdominant males taking up residence in hedgerows.

Females were found to be more abundant in woods than were males, and across all habitat types did not show the same degree of variation in abundance. This may relate to their forming flocks in the areas of best habitat, while the males were scattered throughout all the available cover. Hedgerows contained the highest densities of birds, and woodlands the lowest. However, we stress that our data were collected from four typical estates where pheasant shooting had little influence on woodland management. Whilst hedgerows and game crops appear more important than woodlands in terms of the relative densities of birds which use them, they are both generally small in area, on average about 0.5–1.0 hectare. Woods still attract large numbers of birds

Table 3.4 Relative density ($\bar{x}\pm se$)* of male and female pheasants on four types of pheasant drive during the shooting season. Birds were counted emerging from the four combinations of drives

Drive type	Mean area of drive (ha)	Males	Females	n
Woodland	2.4 ± 0.2	7.8 ± 0.9	10.6 ± 1.7	46
Game crop/hedge	1.0 ± 0.2	16.0 ± 2.0	15.6 ± 1.4	57
Game crop	0.9 ± 0.2	14.9 ± 2.2	15.3 ± 4.2	35
Hedge	0.3 ± 0.1	50.9 ± 22.8	24.4 ± 11.5	14

* calculated as:
$$(N_{obs}/N_{Tobs})100/D$$
where N_{obs} = Number observed on each drive
  N_{Tobs} = Total number observed on the day
  D = Area of drive (ha)

although in Table 3.4 their importance is masked by the fact that woodland drives were, on average, two and a half times larger than those in game crops and eight times the size of hedgerow drives. Woodlands provide the most extensive and important winter cover for pheasants and contain most of the birds although at a lower density than in certain other habitats.

In order to see whether particular structural features in the woodlands led to differences in their use by pheasants, we measured a range of variables within each of the areas driven. On each drive, we measured 18 habitat variables, which related to vegetation structure both inside the habitat (except where hedges were concerned) and on its edge. These variables are described in Table 3.5.

In two multiple regression analyses, using relative male and female densities as the dependent variables, we examined which woodland habitat variables were most closely related to pheasant density. In this approach our results pointed out some interesting

Table 3.5 Variables measured on pheasant drives on the four estates in 1985/86

	Variable	Represented by
Inside	Ground cover	% cover
	Herb layer 1	1−10 cm
	Herb layer 2	11−30 cm
	Herb layer 3	31−100 cm
	Shrub	1 m−2 m
	Understorey	2 m−5 m
	Canopy	>5 m
Edge	Ground cover	% cover
	Herb layer 1	1−10 cm
	Herb layer 2	11−30 cm
	Herb layer 3	31−100 cm
	Shrub	1 m−2 m
	Understorey	2 m−5 m
	Canopy	>5 m
Number of feeder outlets		n
Length of edge		m
Distance from edge to first large trees		m
Area of drive		ha

differences between the sexes. Relative male density was influenced most by the provision of food, as measured by the number of feeding hopper outlets on the drive (Table 3.6a). The length of edge around the woodland had a secondary positive effect. By contrast the shrub layer was the most important factor influencing relative female density, most probably because woods with little shrub vegetation are cold, draughty and offer little cover (Table 3.6b). The number of feeding hopper outlets had a secondary positive effect, so groups of females also respond to food availability. These findings are illustrated in Figs 3.5 and 3.6.

Other studies support the conclusions outlined above. On Lyons Estate, a total of 564 pheasants were caught in 88 cage

Table 3.6 Multiple regression analysis of relative density of (a) males and (b) females in relation to vegetation structure and food from woodland drives, both inside and on the edge

(a) Males		Partial regression coefficient
Feeding hopper outlets		1.85^{**}
Herb 3 (edge)		-0.30^{*}
Edge length		0.01^{*}
Herb 1 (inside)		0.11^{ns}
Understorey cover (edge)		0.13^{ns}
Shrub cover (edge)		0.10^{ns}
Herb 2 (edge)		0.06^{ns}
	Constant	5.24
	df	45
	r	0.79^{**}

(b) Females		Partial regression coefficient
Shrub cover (inside)		0.59^{**}
Feeding hopper outlets		1.62^{**}
Herb 2 (inside)		-1.60^{ns}
Herb 3 (inside)		-0.20^{ns}
Herb 1 (inside)		0.12^{ns}
Shrub cover (edge)		-0.23^{ns}
Ground cover (edge)		-0.23^{ns}
	Constant	31.95
	df	45
	r	0.69^{**}

* $P<0.01$
** $P<0.001$
ns not significant

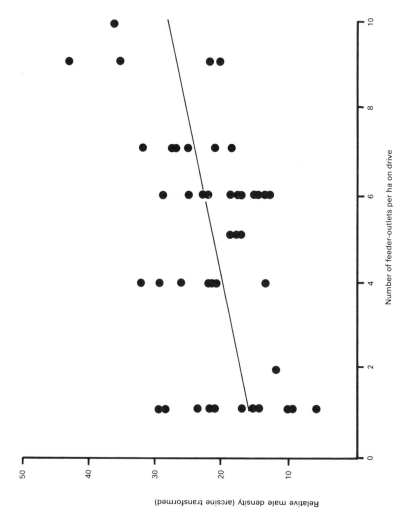

Fig. 3.5 Male pheasants were more likely to emerge from habitats which had a large number of feeding hoppers than from those which had few.

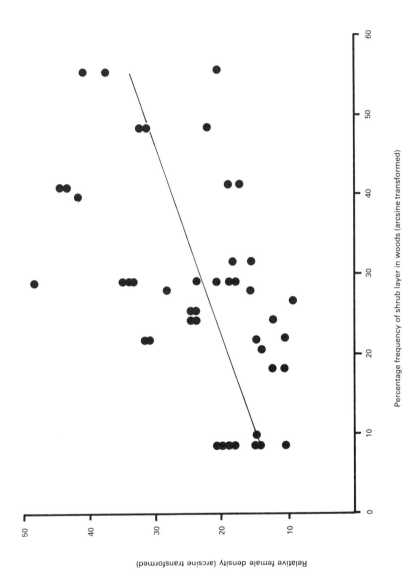

Fig. 3.6 Female density was higher in woods with a well developed shrub layer than in woods where the shrub layer was absent or sparse.

traps in late winter (Robertson 1985a). These data can be used to
examine pheasant use of different cover types. Traps were placed
in six different habitat types: scrub, woodland with a shrubby
understorey, woodland with a bare understorey and ground layer,
woodland with a grazed grassy ground layer, hedgerow, and lastly,
open agricultural habitats. Preference indices for pheasant use of
each habitat type were calculated using the method described by
Jacobs (1974). This gives a value of between 0 and 1 if a habitat is
selected for and between -1 and 0 if it is avoided. Figure 3.7
shows how pheasants used the six habitat categories outlined
above. There was significant selection for scrub and woodland
with a scrub understorey, while all the others were significantly
avoided ($P<0.001$, Neu, Byers and Peek 1974). This emphasises
pheasant use of permanent cover during the winter and the selection of shrubby cover.

These data can also be used to compare the habitat selection of
males and females (Fig. 3.8). Males were caught significantly
more often in scrub ($X^2=13.14$, $df=1$, $P<0.001$) and females more

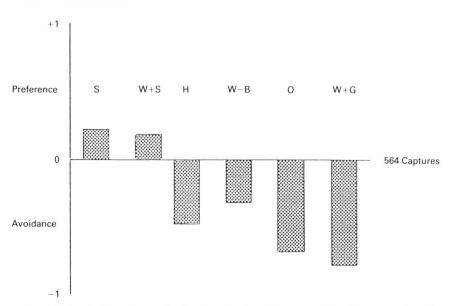

Jacob's Preference Index

Fig. 3.7 Scrub (S) and woodland with a shrub understorey (W+S) were preferred
habitats of pheasants on the Lyons Estate, whereas hedges (H), bare woodland
(W−B), open fields (O) and woodland with a grass herb layer (W+G) were
avoided.

Jacob's Preference Index

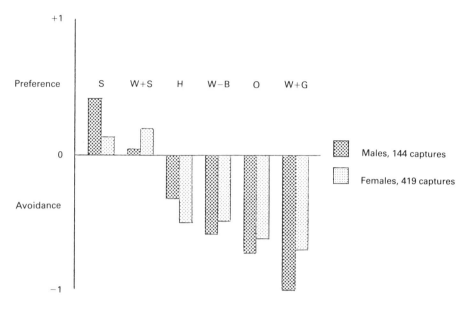

Fig. 3.8 At Lyons, males preferred scrub and females preferred woodland with a shrubby understorey, the two sexes showing significant differences in their preference of habitats.

frequently in woodland with a shrubby understorey ($X^2=9.15$, $df=1$, $P<0.01$). On the Lyons study area, shrubs were found in small, fragmented plots compared to the larger blocks of woodland. The differences in habitat selection between the sexes may reflect the dispersed nature of the males compared to the concentration of hens within the best habitats, as described previously.

Finally, these data also cast more light on the behaviour of young and old hens (Fig. 3.9). Although both ages of females preferred woodland with a shrub understorey, the young hens also selected scrub, a habitat type that was avoided by the older birds. This may relate to the older hens forming stable flocks in the best habitats while the younger birds, who are also more inclined to be 'drifters', move out into less favourable habitats.

It is not only the structure of the wood that is attractive to pheasants. The importance of woodland edges to this bird has also been clearly demonstrated by radiotracking. Studies of radio-marked birds in the winter of 1986/7 clearly show how they spend the majority of their time within 20 m of the boundaries between

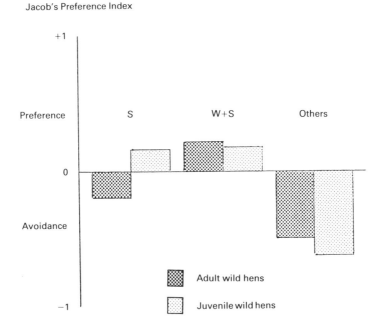

Fig. 3.9 A comparison of winter habitat selection of adult and juvenile wild hen pheasants at the Lyons Estate.

woodland and open ground (Fig. 3.10). Their use of these edge habitats was highly significant. There was also preferential, although not significant, use of those areas between 20 and 50 m of the woodland edge (Robertson 1988a). These data also demonstrate the avoidance of bare, agricultural habitats during the winter months. This selection for woodland edge will affect the holding capacity of different sized woods. Our winter shoot analysis supports this. Woods covering less than 1.5 ha contained higher relative pheasant densities of both cocks and hens than did larger woods (Figs 3.11a and b). Small woods, by their very nature, have a higher 'edge to area ratio'. Large woods, on the other hand, often contain areas which are far from any woodland edge and of little use to pheasants. The influence of woodland size will doubtless have important implications for the design of game coverts and their integration with other forms of land-use, a topic to which we shall return in a later chapter.

These findings on winter social behaviour and habitat selection have important implications for pheasant management during the

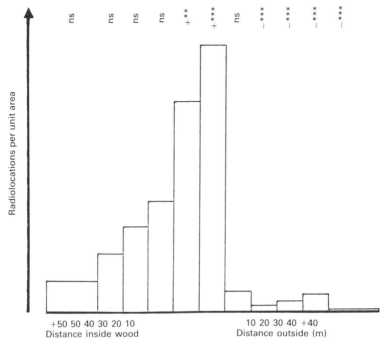

Fig. 3.10 Preference for edge habitats during the winter was shown by locating radiomarked males and females at Clarendon Park, Wiltshire.

winter period. Pheasants do not appear to like a woodland with a dense herb layer, i.e. up to approximately 0.5 m in height. The reason we believe the shrub layer is so important is that it provides both sheltered places in which to rest and a relatively open ground so that pheasants can gain access to whatever food is available.

HABITAT AND OVERWINTER SURVIVAL

One possible reason why pheasants use sheltered habitats such as coverts and woodlands may be to avoid the rigours of harsh winter weather, although a number of studies have found no relationship between a winter warmth index and an index of survival (Wood and Brotherson 1981). These workers found that the overwinter survival of birds was independent of their density during the winter over a limited area in Utah which implies that competition for food in this situation is not important. In general

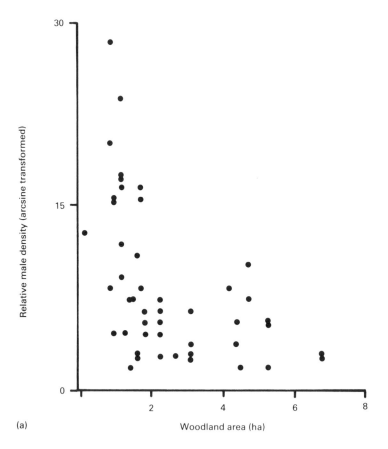

Fig. 3.11 As the size of woodland increases the relative density of (a) males and (b) females declines.

they were able to conclude that survival rates in winter were highly variable and that winter weather had little influence on pheasant populations.

In other parts of America, harsh weather has been shown to cause much higher mortality of hens in late winter (Edwards *et al.* 1964, Gates and Woehler 1968, Gates 1971) and, as we have already mentioned, poor weather at this time can delay the onset of laying. Vulnerability to predators can also increase in birds under stress as a result of prolonged severe weather (Dumke and Pils 1973).

Habitat obviously has an important role to play in reducing the

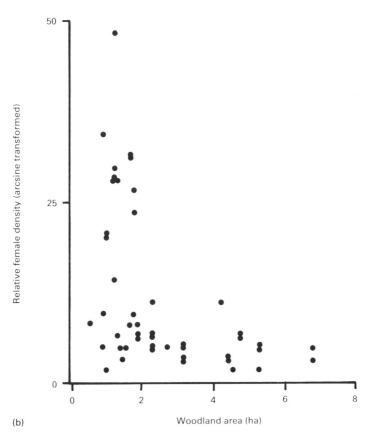

Fig. 3.11(b).

effects of severe weather by providing shelter. Observations by conservation officers in the first two weeks of severe storms in the Great Plains of the United States showed that the only large concentrations of surviving pheasants were in windbreaks and 'treeclaims' or coverts. Most of the coverts specifically planted for pheasants in the USA are less than 30 m wide and cover less than a quarter of a hectare. A study designed to investigate the use of 'woody plantings' by wintering pheasants in the USA also showed that the best coverts were those which were positioned so as not to attract snow drifts, and that those surrounded by weedy arable land were preferred to those surrounded by pasture (Lyon 1959).

Estimates of overwinter survival are not readily available largely because of the difficulty in separating out the effects of shooting-related and natural mortality. One study in the USA showed that 36% of total annual mortality occurred during the period when snow covered the ground, which represented proportionally more of the total than that caused by shooting (Dumke and Pils 1973). Late winter mortality (mid-February to mid-April) represented 12% of total annual losses.

Where less extreme weather conditions exist it appears that overwinter loss may be related more to pheasant density. At Knoll Farm, Damerham, we have been trapping birds in winter and fitting them with numbered fin-tabs. From mark and recapture analyses we have estimates of the early spring breeding population. This work has been conducted for a period of only five winters, but it is evident that significant density-dependent overwinter loss occurs (Fig. 3.12). This is calculated as the loss to the population (in logarithms), although we cannot separate death from losses caused by birds dispersing from the area, nor gains by birds dispersing into the area occurring from autumn to the following spring. This is not unexpected; density-dependent over-winter loss has been shown to occur in a number of species which 'defend' breeding territories or sites in the spring and whose autumn populations fluctuate between years as a result of random factors affecting chick production (Hill 1984b, and in press).

Habitat and survival are therefore linked in two ways. First, woodlands and coverts with well developed and abundant shrub layers can probably reduce direct mortality under extreme environmental conditions. Certainly there is evidence that pheasants select them in preference to more open habitats which afford less protection from the vagaries of the climate. Second, there is evidence that overwinter loss, whether as a result of mortality or perhaps more importantly as a result of greater dispersal, is higher when birds live at high density, and when habitat shortage in the spring is limiting, the opportunities for territory establishment are significantly reduced.

PREDATION

One of the reasons why pheasants inhabit cover during the winter period, unrelated to the shelter it provides against cold weather,

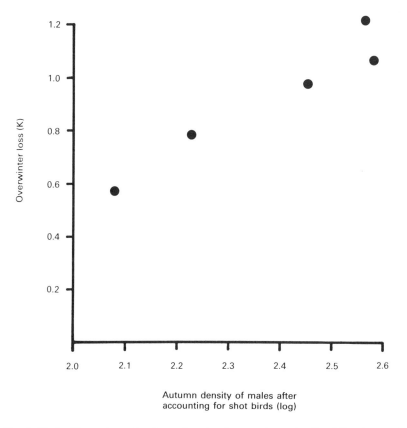

Fig. 3.12 At Damerham the loss of males from autumn to the following spring was found to be dependent on the density of birds in autumn.

is presumably to reduce the risks of predation. Use of low ground and shrub cover and the cryptic plumage of the female is believed to have survival advantages, while feeding in the open makes them more likely to be detected by a predator. One of the reasons why they feed in groups in open habitats, particularly during the winter, is presumably because of the advantages of having many pairs of eyes to keep watch. The improved vigilance gained by individuals in a flock also means that more time can be spent feeding and the crop can be filled more quickly, which will decrease the amount of time each bird needs to spend in the open.

In their introduced range, winter predation has only received attention from a few studies. Work on the diet of predators has also yielded information regarding the composition of the various foods consumed, one of which is the pheasant.

The fox is undoubtedly the most important predator of pheasants except in those areas where certain raptors reach high densities. A study of radiotagged pheasants in Wisconsin in North America showed that predation caused 79% of all winter deaths in a pheasant population (Dumke and Pils 1973). Mammalian predators, mostly foxes, accounted for 38% of these deaths, while 28% were attributed to raptors. Their study also revealed seasonal differences in the rates of pheasant mortality. Most predation, both avian and mammalian, occurred when the ground was covered with snow. Mammalian predation during late winter and nesting was also high but declined during brood-rearing and post brood-rearing periods in the annual cycle (Fig. 3.13).

The effect of goshawk predation on both wild and hand-reared pheasants has been studied in much more detail. By radiotagging goshawks in Sweden, Kenward (1977) and Kenward et al. (1981) neatly showed that the non-territoriality and range overlap of these raptors in winter created core areas of predator activity,

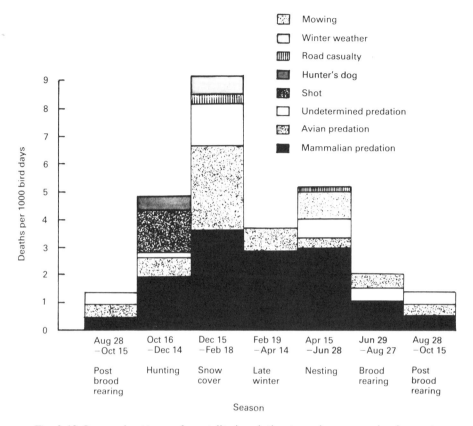

Fig. 3.13 Seasonal patterns of mortality in relation to various causes in pheasants studied in the United States. (Redrawn from Dumke and Pils 1973.)

causing locally heavy predation of pheasants. When hand-reared pheasants were first released the hawks showed no preference for either male or female poults, presumably because there is little difference in appearance or size. As the poults grew and attained adult weight, the goshawks selected the lighter females. Male goshawks are smaller and lighter in weight than females and Kenward showed that their predation rate on pheasants fell from 0.58 birds per day in August when mainly smaller poults were available, to 0.05 per day in January. Male goshawks were shown to consume pheasants at an average of 133 g/day compared to 189 g/day eaten by females, slightly above the calculated requirements of each sex of 120 g/day and 160 g/day respectively in the mid-winter period.

Goshawks did not appear to selectively kill pheasants in poor condition. Kenward argues that this was because most kills (82%) were the result of surprise attacks made either in dense cover or close to cover, so that there was little chance of a chase which might have made selection for poor condition possible. In goshawk attacks on wood-pigeon flocks he showed that there was no selection for poor condition when pigeons were taken before they flew away, but that selection did increase as the amount of surprise in the attack declined (Kenward 1978).

Predation by goshawks was shown to account for 88% of the 64% overwinter loss of female pheasants and 23% of the 76% loss of males on his Swedish study area, representing 56% of their autumn population. On average, each goshawk took 0.43 pheasants per day but both the predation rate and the time spent feeding increased for hawks living near pheasant release sites where there were high densities of prey. In terms of biomass, pheasants were the most important prey of goshawks in this area. However, local differences including the density of buffer prey species such as hares, are thought to have a significant effect on the predation of pheasants. On Gotland, rabbits increase predation on pheasants by drawing in hawks which incidentally take pheasants if they are about (Kenward 1986). High levels of disease in some pheasant populations have also been reputed to have contributed to high goshawk predation levels (Göransson 1975).

Whilst raptor predation in Britain is not an important mortality factor, the current increase in the goshawk population might cause some local concern, although it is very doubtful that the situation would reach economic significance as was the case in Kenward's study. Foxes, on the other hand, represent a more widespread and significant problem with, in many instances, important economic implications to the shoot.

It is important to realise that while predation can be important to the numbers of pheasants surviving the winter period, the contribution they make to the total annual consumption of food of most predators can be small. This has been illustrated best by a study in Sweden in which the number of prey individuals eaten by the whole range of predators in one area was assessed (Erlinge et al. 1984). They found that although 60% of subadult-adult pheasants in autumn were consumed by predators (two-thirds of this figure being attributed to foxes) this represented only 1% of the estimated total annual prey consumption. In other words the predators were important to the pheasant, but pheasants were not that important to the predators. The relative importances are bound, however, to be inextricably linked to the availability of buffer prey species. For example, fluctuations in the abundance of rabbits, the main prey species, would doubtless have affected the relative importance of other prey items in the diet of the predators.

4   Finding Mates

One feature of pheasants that makes them particularly interesting is their rather rare type of breeding and mating system. It is based on the defence of harems of females by territorial males and is therefore called 'territorial harem defence polygyny', where polygyny indicates that some males may breed with more than one female in the same season. Its peculiar breeding habits have been known for many years; indeed, one doyen of British ornithology, Lord Grey of Fallodon, wrote, in his book '*The Charm of Birds*':

'British birds are monogamous: this is the rule and exceptions are few... Pheasants...need not be taken into account; the inferiority of their habits is not native to Britain, and our country is not responsible for them' (1927)

Many species of birds once believed to be monogamous have since been found to have a more complicated breeding arrangement. However, the pheasant must have always been considered one of the few which did things differently because of the obvious way in which males strut about on the edges of cover, escorting their hens.

What are the factors which may make pheasants use this unusual system? It has been suggested for mammals such as the yellow-bellied marmot that polygyny has evolved merely because females prefer to live in groups (Elliot 1975), and a similar interpretation has been given to pheasant polygyny by some authors (Oring 1982). Alternatively, if a male can monopolise some vital resource then he may be able to attract more than one female to breed with him. In many other polygynous birds territory quality is an important determinant of male success in attracting a harem (Verner 1964, Orians 1969, Wittenberger 1979, Garson *et al.* 1981). Territory quality in male pheasants could be related to the amount and type of nutritious food provided for females during the spring when they are producing eggs, or to the amount of nesting cover available.

Some recent work conducted by Matt Ridley at the Edward Grey Institute at the University of Oxford, and continued by ourselves, has looked at these explanations, together with the quality of the male himself in guarding females by looking out for predators or other males intent on harassing them. We have investigated this mate guarding facility provided by the male in relation to determining the number of mates he is likely to attract (Ridley 1983, Ridley and Hill 1987).

This chapter shows how females obtain and choose mates, how harems are formed, what qualifies as a territory, and what qualities of the male are important to hens during the spring.

POST-WINTER DISPERSAL OF FEMALES

One of the most important seasons for movement in pheasant populations occurs during late March and early April when females disperse from their winter flocks. The average group size of females during this time declines from about six to just over two. In fact most hens are still in groups of two or more birds in May (Fig. 4.1). From using large overlapping winter ranges they move to smaller widely spaced breeding ranges (Fig. 4.2) during which time they associate much more with males. The proportion of female groups being escorted by males increases from about 40% in late February to over 85% in mid-May, the time when breeding activity is at its peak.

During this period of dispersal it is generally the immature females which move the furthest. At Fulwell 9 immature females moved an average of 309 ± 126 metres from their winter ranges to breeding ranges. In comparison, 11 adult females moved an average of 196 ± 138 metres (significant at $P<0.05$).

When the females disperse and join harems they also move out of woodlands in favour of more open habitats (Fig. 4.3). At this time the males establish their territories at the edges of permanent cover such as woodlands and open habitats such as cereal fields or pasture. Females require a diet consisting predominantly of young shoots which, in the arable landscapes which we have studied, are provided by growing cereal crops. Even in their native lands such food can only be obtained from more open habitats, and their social organisation is largely a result of the way in which they need to exploit food in habitats which leave them prone to predation and disturbance. We shall discuss this in more detail shortly.

POST-WINTER DISPERSAL OF MALES

Males disperse after the winter to establish their breeding territories. In many areas there are more males than potential territories, and those unsuccessful in establishing a territory either disperse to find space elsewhere, or else remain non-territorial.

From our observations of males caught and fin-tabbed at Damerham, over a five-year period (1983–1987 inclusive), the

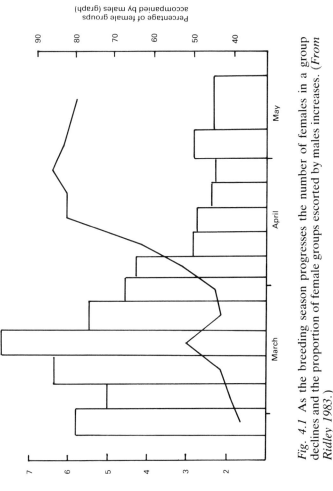

Fig. 4.1 As the breeding season progresses the number of females in a group declines and the proportion of female groups escorted by males increases. (*From Ridley 1983.*)

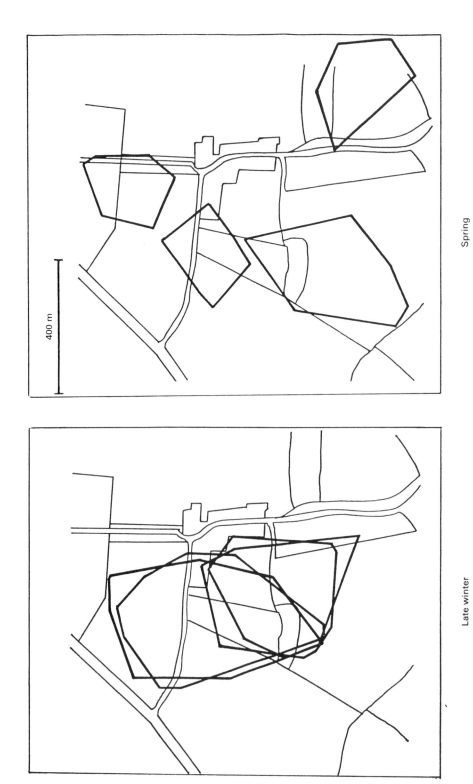

400 m

Late winter

Spring

Fig. 4.2 After occupying large overlapping ranges in winter these four radiotagged hens dispersed in spring into smaller non-overlapping ranges. (*From Ridley 1983.*)

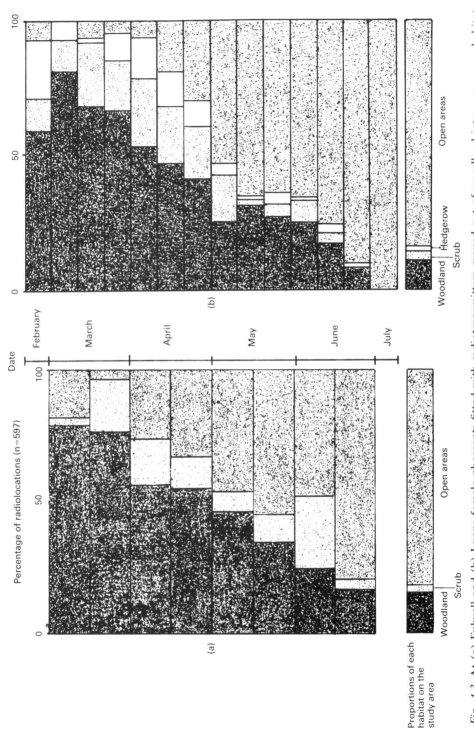

Fig. 4.3 At (a) Fulwell and (b) Lyons female pheasants fitted with radiotransmitters moved out of woodland into more open habitats and cereal fields as the breeding season progressed.

number of territorial males has remained relatively constant, averaging 14 per 100 hectares, whilst the numbers of non-territorial males has fluctuated dramatically but is generally larger following years when birds are released (Table 4.1). The proportion of the male population establishing a territory is therefore dependent on the density of birds in early spring. This appears to operate by some members of the male population failing to obtain a breeding space when the population is at a high density.

Non-territorial males disperse further from their winter range (317±53 metres) than old territory-owning males (133±25 metres) but about the same distance as males which obtain territories for the first time. A male which has already had a territory in a previous year generally moves less far between ranges in successive springs (66±27 metres) than a male which has become territorial for the first time (230±50 metres) (Hill and Ridley 1987).

So, during the late winter/early spring period there is a great deal of activity in pheasant populations. Females generally disperse further than males and immatures move further than adults. One of the main reasons for these movements is related to males establishing territories along the edges of permanent cover and females choosing mates with which to breed.

Table 4.1 Territory, harem sizes and overwinter loss in relation to the extent of rearing on the Damerham study area, 1983–1987

	1983	1984	1985	1986	1987
Released in Previous Summer	600	800	0	1000	950
Territorial Males	30	23	31	31	29
Non-Territorial Males (% of Total)	32(52%)	55(70%)	11(26%)	88(72%)	39(57%)
Mean Harem Size (± SE)	2.2(0.2)	3.3(0.5)	3.3(0.3)	3.0(0.3)	3.2(0.3)
Male Population in Previous Autumn	442	528	134	641	553
Female Population in Previous Autumn	433	551	146	624	537
Overwinter Loss in Male Population	0.660	0.689	0.453	0.542	0.413
Overwinter Loss in Female Population	0.377	0.702	0.185	0.307	0.665

MALES, TERRITORIES AND AGGRESSION

An animal defends a territory for a reason: to monopolise food, breeding habitat, mating sites or some other resource. Furthermore, a territorial male achieves polygynous status either by attracting several females to breed in his territory or by defending a resource or site which is visited by a succession of females (Wittenberger 1979).

While density-dependence has been shown to occur in our intensively studied population, other studies have shown that although males have restricted ranges they often exist at a low density where territories are not contiguous but spaced out, with unused habitats in between (Lachlan and Bray 1976). Other studies have found them to be loosely territorial at high densities (Baskett 1947). A study of the literature (expanding on Ridley

Table 4.2 Literature summary of territory size and male density (nos per 100 ha) in the pheasant (After Ridley 1983)

Area	Male density	Non-territorial males?	Territory size (ha)	Reference
California USA	1.2	?	1.2–5.3	Twining 1946
Wisconsin USA	13.0	yes	2.4–4.8	Taber 1949
Wisconsin USA	11.1	no	1.9	Burger 1964
Wisconsin USA	19.7	yes	1.4	Burger 1964
Ontario Canada	95.0	no	2.4–4.5	Ball 1950
Sweden	6.9	yes	5.2	Goransson 1980
Dorset UK	28.0	yes	1.8	Lachlan and Bray 1976
Dorset UK	13.0	yes	2.5	Lachlan and Bray 1973
Oxfordshire UK	41.0	yes	2.0	Ridley 1983
Hampshire UK	14.0	yes	2.5	Hill 1984
Co. Kildare Ireland	2.3	yes	4.5	Robertson 1986

1983) shows that male density varies dramatically but that territory size is relatively constant and in most populations studied some members remain non-territorial (Table 4.2). Within study areas smaller territories are generally correlated with higher territorial male density (Seubert 1952, Burger 1964, Lachlan and Bray 1976). There is consequently a 'compression' of territories as more males try to establish themselves within a particular area.

Figure 4.4 shows the distribution of male territories on Knoll Farm. Territories are established only in certain habitats along woodland edges. As such, territories contain both permanent cover and more open areas. The open habitats provide areas where males can display to females and proclaim their territories, as well as feeding sites for hens (Fig. 4.5). Territories tend to have a greater number of different habitat types than expected

Fig. 4.4 The territories of male pheasants observed on the Damerham study area, showing little overlap.

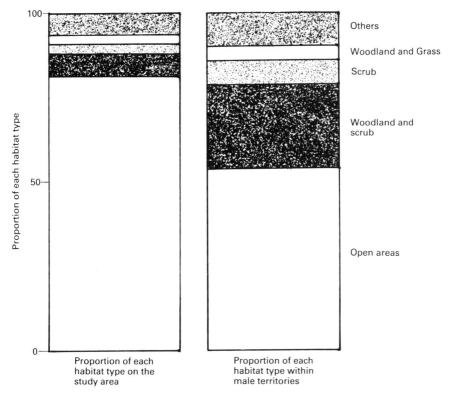

Fig. 4.5 Habitat composition of territories on Lyons Estate, showing that scrub and woodland was more common in territories than in the study area as a whole, while open areas were used more rarely.

from random (Fig. 4.6). So it appears that males are selecting areas with a diversity of cover types.

So why are some males territorial and others non-territorial? At Fulwell, Ridley found that 60% of males holding territories for the first time were adults whilst only 13% of non-territorial males were adults. As well as being generally older, territory holders are also slightly heavier than their non-territorial counterparts (Table 4.3). So it appears to be the older and heavier males which gain territories while younger birds often remain non-territorial.

It is possible to identify three distinct types of territory depending on the amount of different cover relating to woodland edge, hedgerow and clearing. There tends to be no difference in territory

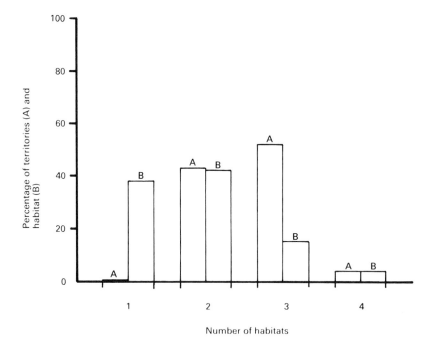

Fig. 4.6 Male territories contained significantly more habitat types than did a series of 2 ha grid squares on the Fulwell study area, suggesting that territories are situated on habitat boundaries, specifically at the edges of cover. Open bars = territories, hatched bars = habitat. (X^2=16.9, $P<$0.001, 3 df.) (*From Ridley 1983.*)

Table 4.3 Comparison of weights and home range size in April (number of 0.45 ha squares occupied) of non-territorial males with males holding territories for the first time

	Non-territorial males	Males holding territory for first time
Age	12.5% adult (n=16)	60.0% adult (n=15)
Body weight (g) in previous winter (mean ± SE)	1450 ± 93	1482 ± 106
Home range size	23.2	11.8

size between these categories. Ridley found that of the whole of his study area, only open ground more than 150 m from cover, and mixed woodland more than 50 m from open ground remains undefended by mid-April, at which point he calculated that 98% of the boundaries between cover and open ground (including hedgerows but excluding clearings) were occupied. Open spaces are a major component of territories, as is shrubby cover (Fig. 4.7). Male use of such habitats in spring may therefore be related to the presence of females to which he can monopolise mating access. It is obviously important in breeding terms for males to be in the right place at the right time in the spring, and they may well be able to assess an area's attractiveness to females prior to the females actually moving into the area to breed.

As the proportion of a male's boundary which is shared with a neighbour increases, so territory size declines (Fig. 4.8) and there is a positive correlation between male body weight in the previous winter and territory size ($r=0.66$, $P<0.05$, Ridley 1983) such that heavier males defend larger territories. Territory size tends also to be related to age; for eight males watched in two consecutive years territory size increased from 1.89 ± 0.32 ha to 2.31 ± 0.27 ha (significant at $P<0.01$) but, as we shall show later, the increase in territory size gained by older males is not nearly

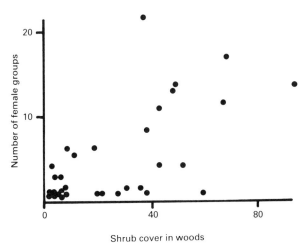

Fig. 4.7 In spring the amount of shrub cover in woodland is important to the number of female groups which use it.

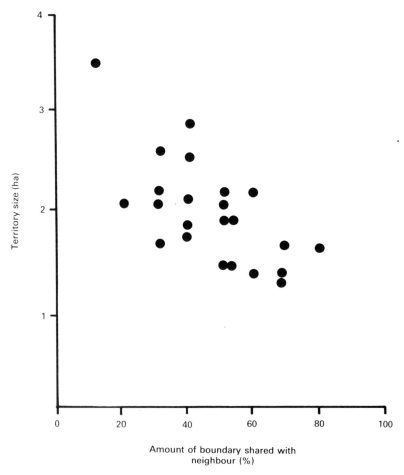

Fig. 4.8 Isolated territories of males with few neighbours are larger than those with neighbours on all sides, suggesting that territories can become compressed in size. (Redrawn from Ridley 1983.)

enough to account for the dramatic differences in the number of females that they attract. Immatures also begin crowing later than adults which suggests that early claim to a territory is confined to older males.

Because territories are both associated with woodland edge and are of small size, non-territorial males feed further from any cover (65.4 $\pm$ 32.6 metres) than territorial males (27.9 $\pm$ 30.8 metres; $P<0.01$), and this is quite striking when watching a woodland edge frequented by pheasants. On early morning watches it is possible to observe the harem-defending territorial males closely guarding their precious hens, whilst the less fortunate non-territorial males are already well into the centre of the field. These males often associate together, and this presumably confers greater protection because of increased vigilance. Feeding a long way from cover is presumably forced upon them because almost all of the available boundary habitats are taken up by territorial birds and they are not tolerated in these areas. Feeding in the open in this way could be quite dangerous as there is little cover to afford escape from predators. Birds of prey would perhaps find it easier to attack a pheasant whilst in the open. Indeed, we have had a number of reports of pheasants being reluctant to emerge from a wood when goshawks were in residence. It would be interesting to know whether predators hunted the non-territorial male population more successfully as a consequence of their spending more time out in the open.

Non-territorial males demonstrate other differences from their territorial counterparts. The most obvious relate to their submissive nature. They do not inflate their wattles to anything like the extent of territorial males and do not erect their pinnae (ear-tufts). Much of a territorial male's display aims to make him seem

Plate V. A territorial male pheasant with fully inflated wattles. (*P.A. Robertson*)

larger than life and he fluffs out his feathers and stands upright to
achieve this. In comparison, the non-territorial males often seem
skinny and sleek with their heads down and feathers flat against
the body.

How then do territorial males defend their boundaries? They
do this by means of a set of aggressive behaviour patters. Aggressive displays are generally considered to reduce the risk of
injury by asserting status or territory ownership. In pheasants, an
escalating series of displays is used, culminating in a physical
attack if the intruder does not flee. These have been described by
Taber (1949) and Ridley (1983); their seasonal frequencies are
shown in Fig. 4.9 and include:

(1) Walk threat. The male (territory holder) approaches the
    intruder with head and tail held high; later in the season this
    takes the form of a run threat. The intruder's response is
    usually to crouch to avoid detection; when the threatening
    male comes close the intruder flees or adopts a submissive
    posture.
(2) Peck threat. If the intruder does not flee, the threatening
    male sometimes moves up to him, intermittently pecking at
    the ground.
(3) Lateral strut. If the intruder remains, the resident moves
    slowly across his front, with body and tail feathers tilted and
    wing trailing on the side nearest the intruder. This is similar
    to, but should be differentiated from, the 'lateral display'
    used in courtship.
(4) Aerial chase. As a last resort the resident male takes to the
    air to chase off the intruder.

Boundary disputes between neighbouring territorial males are
more frequent during territory establishment than during harem
formation, and of 15 uninterrupted fights recorded by Ridley, the
average duration was 18 minutes. On Fulwell, most fights involving adults were boundary disputes, whilst those involving immatures were generally attempts to establish a territory.

Males announce their territories and their harems by crowing.
The crowing call has two syllables and the call is audible at up to
2 km. Sonograms of the calls show pronounced individuality
which may enable the female to recognise her mate. Certainly, it
is possible to distinguish different males by ear. (Red junglefowl

Escaile Hudson

Above left: A territorial male pheasant standing guard over a female whilst she feeds. (*P.A. Robertson*)

Above right: Female pheasants spend the winter in woodlands with well developed shrub layers. (*D.A. Hill*)

Left: Fitting a fin tab to a female pheasant, enabling her to be individually identified in the field. (*D.A. Hill*)

Right: Pheasant chicks require insect food during the first 10 days of life. (*P.A. Robertson*)

Above: Radiomarked pheasants can be accurately located using a directional aerial.
(*P.A. Robertson*)

Right: Pheasants often dump eggs into the nests of other birds, in this case a woodcock's.
(*D.A. Hill*)

Above: Insects and other invertebrates were sampled within the feeding ranges of young broods, using a Dietrick Vacuum Net Sampler. (*P.A. Robertson*)

Below: Large rides provide breeding areas chick rearing habitat. (*D.A. Hill*)

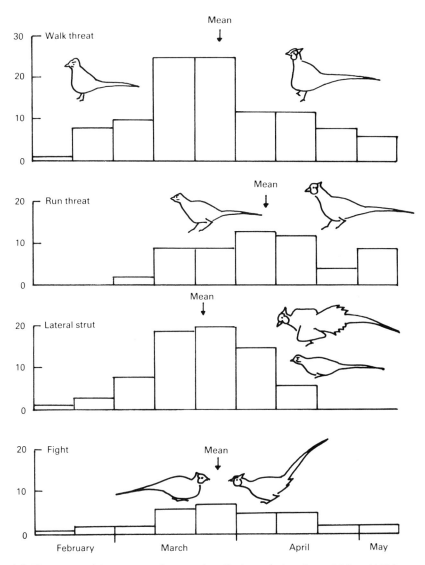

Fig. 4.9 The seasonal frequency of aggressive displays. (taken from Ridley 1983.)

also have a mating system based on harem defence polygyny and again the calls of the males are individually characteristic.) Crowing males can be heard throughout the year but there is a pronounced peak during March, April and May. Most crowing takes place around dawn and to a lesser extent before dusk, but calling birds can be heard at almost any time of the day or night. The crowing call is followed by a short wing drum at about 14 per second which produces a deep, almost subsonic vibration. This does not carry as far as the main call and is only heard at close quarters. Crowing and the associated wing drum in pheasants presumably serves a number of functions including warning off males, attracting females and advertising the position of the male to harem members and neighbours. The major factor affecting crowing rates of males is the presence or absence of females. Matt Ridley showed that territorial males without females present crowed at 1.7 times the rate (with an average interval between crows of 2.63 ± 1.68 minutes) of males whose females were present on his territory.

Whilst it is fairly easy to get a response from a territorial male pheasant by, for example, slamming a car door or producing any other sharp noise, the call produced is different to that of the disyllabic crow call. A cock bird will often make 2–3 loud, but higher pitched, calls just after his neighbour crows. One early American study, however, used this to their advantage. They detonated small explosive charges and were able to locate all the

Plate VI. In the spring male pheasants set up territories along shrubby woodland edges. (*P.A. Robertson*)

breeding males over a certain area at once. Pheasants also appear to be sensitive to the vibrations preceding an earthquake and there are numerous reports of tremors being preceded by raucous calling by the local pheasants.

Territorial males are dominant over others when on their territories even if the intruder had higher winter rank. This territorial dominance rule does break down however, and fights result either when non-territorial males dispute ownership of a vacant territory or when neighbouring territory owners establish mutual boundaries.

In summary: males set up territories along the edges of permanent cover; they maintain ownership of these areas by means of crowing and an escalating series of displays. In most populations a proportion of the younger males do not establish a territory and are forced to live away from the woodland edges.

HAREMS

Female groups show a rapid turn-over during early April as dispersing individuals join and leave harems. However, harem members are often from the same winter flocks. Some territorial males obtain very few or no females whilst others obtain many. Consequently mating opportunities are distributed unevenly across the male population (Fig. 4.10). In other words some males are much better at attracting females than others. From mid-April onwards, females have generally settled into their breeding ranges and by this time on Fulwell fin-tabbed females were observed on 74% of occasions with their particular 'major' male, the one with which they probably eventually copulated. The implication is that settled females are monogamous after reaching their breeding range. About 65% of a female's time is spent on the male's territory (based on observations of radiotagged females) and consequently 35% of time is spent outside it. Females usually leave the male's territory to nest and their home ranges (2.9 ± 0.8 ha) are generally larger than male territories (2.0 ± 0.5 ha; $n=23$, $P<0.01$).

The average harem size at Fulwell, after accounting for the lower visibility of hens compared to cocks, was about 2.4 ± 0.4 hens. However, this value varies dramatically between studies. Westerskov (1956) reports a mean harem size of only just over 1

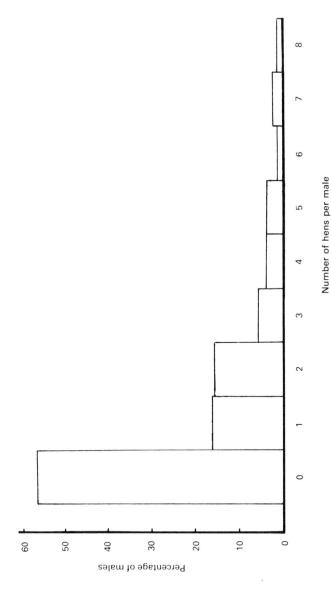

Fig. 4.10 Mating opportunities are distributed unevenly across the male population, a feature of the pheasant's mating system. Some males obtain a large number of females whereas many obtain none. (*From Ridley and Hill 1987.*)

Plate VII. Females usually move away from the male's territory in order to nest. (*D.A. Hill*)

in New Zealand, while Robertson (1986) found an average of 4.9 ± 0.5 hens in each harem in Ireland. One might expect that certain types of territories, related to differences in habitat types, would be more attractive to females than others, but we have since found that there are generally no differences in harem size between woodland edge, hedgerow or woodland clearing territory-holding males (Ridley and Hill 1987).

COURTSHIP DISPLAYS

There are generally three types of display performed by males to females during courtship:

(1) Ritual approach. Territorial males walk directly towards females with their head held high and their pinnae erect. This is often a preliminary to the lateral display.
(2) Lateral display. The male approaches the female and moves slowly across her front, spreading his tail and the wing closest

to her. The head is held low and the wattles and pinnae prominently erect. Sometimes the male performs the display while running up to and past the female – the 'run lateral display'.

(3) Tid-bitting. This is a ritualistic courtship feeding behaviour. The head is held low, still and partly on one side as the male calls the female to a morsel of food.

Another type of behaviour involving rape attempts is also observed without preliminary display by either sex, where a male chases a female and attempts to mount her while she attempts to escape.

The type of display performed by a male to a female depends on the size of the group of which the female is a member (Ridley 1983). Ritual approaches are made to females in all group sizes whereas lateral displays are performed mostly to single females (Table 4.4). Unfamiliar females on their own often elicit lateral displays, and these are seen mostly during March and early April (Fig. 4.11). Tid-bitting occurs later in the season and generally is restricted to a female which has formed a bond with the particular territorial male. Tid-bitting coincides with the peak in copulation, which is initiated by the female squatting in front of the displaying male. In Ridley's study, of 17 mating attempts involving marked females, 12 female-solicited matings were between marked females and the males with which they were usually seen, whereas rape attempts were generally between the male and a female not normally seen in his territory. In other words males tried to rape strange females (possibly birds from other harems), but were 'invited' to fertilise their own harem members.

Table 4.4 The type of display performed by a male pheasant to a female depends on the size of the group of which the female is a member. Ritual approaches are made to females in all group sizes, whereas lateral displays are performed mostly to single females (significant at $P<0.001$) (From Ridley 1983)

	Female group size		
	1	2–4	>4
No. ritual approaches seen	14	14	5
No. lateral displays seen	71	9	5

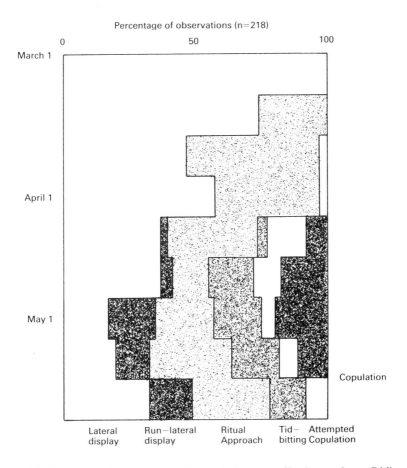

Percentage of observations (n=218)

Fig. 4.11 The seasonal frequency of sexual displays. (Redrawn from Ridley 1983)

CHOOSING A MATE

The fact that females confine most of their activities to one male's territory during mating and egg laying suggests that there is a bond between each female and one particular male which may continue in subsequent seasons. The factors which determine the choice of a male by a female are complicated and interrelated, but can, for convenience, be split into those resources of the male or his territory which we feel might be important in a female's choice. These are: (1) the provision of food supplies, (2) the provision of nesting cover, (3) territory ownership and previous experience, and (4) mate guarding.

If females first choose a breeding site and then mate with a local male, male success in gaining females and successfully achieving copulation would depend on the quality of his territory. There is some evidence for this. On two occasions at Fulwell harems abandoned their mates for neighbours in whose territories barley seeds had recently been sown (Fig. 4.12). However, in another case two females were found with the same male in two consecutive years despite a change in the position of his territory. Both sites included the same crops (spring sown barley) in both years, so a change in territory quality is unlikely to have been responsible. The females were loyal to the male and not solely the territory. Of nine females whose mates were known in two consecutive years, four returned to the same mate and five changed mates, but in all the latter cases their previous mate had disappeared during the year. This suggests that females are loyal to surviving partners in successive years and that food supplies on the territory play only a minor role in mate choice. This is supported by calculations presented by Lachlan and Bray (1976)

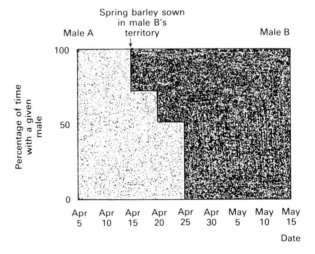

Fig. 4.12 Four females actually changed their mate after spring barley was sown in an adjacent male's territory, although generally food provision on the male's territory plays little role in the number of females which he attracts. (*From Ridley 1983*)

which suggest the average male's territory contains sufficient growing shoots to support 40 hens throughout the breeding season.

Females do not appear to select males on the basis of the provision of nesting habitat within the territory because they generally nest on the periphery of their own feeding range (Chapter 5). In five cases of nine radiotracked females at Fulwell, the nest was placed in the territory of the second most frequently visited male, while in only two cases was it in the major mate's territory. The remaining two females nested beyond the territories of both the major male and the second most frequently visited male.

Males which had held a territory at Fulwell in previous years generally had larger harems (2.12 females, $n=9$) than new territory owners (0.27 females, $n=7$, $P<0.01$). Established males were also more attractive to both adult and immature females. In Sweden, Frömberg and Helgee (1985) demonstrated a similar effect. They found that those males which were dominant during the winter obtained the vast majority of mating opportunities. Whilst we have already mentioned that established territory owners have larger territories than new territory owners, the difference (20%) is not sufficient to account for the huge difference (685%) in harem size based on the hypothesis that larger territories happened to include more female ranges. Also heavier males do not appear to obtain more females.

It appears that the quality of the male himself is the major factor influencing harem size. It would appear to be his ability to guard females against the risk of predation while feeding in the open, of rape attempts from intruding males, and the energy expenditure incurred by taking rapid evasive action from both of these causes that is in some way attractive to the female. Territorial males spend significantly more time alert and less time feeding than either non-territorial males or the females they are escorting. Lone females and females in groups which are not escorted by territorial males spend nearly 10 times more time in alert behaviour looking around for predators and intruding males, and they feed for only one-third the time of females which are escorted by territorial males (Fig. 4.13).

Pheasants are too large to conceal themselves in the vegetation on which they feed during the spring, so they rely on vigilance to detect predators and, in the case of females, non-territorial males

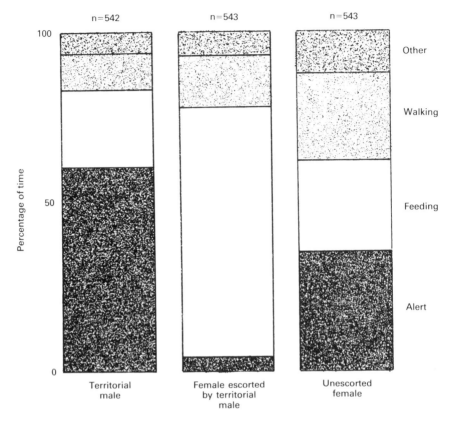

Fig. 4.13 The activity budgets of pheasant at Damerham during April, showing that females being guarded by males spent nearly one-tenth as much time alert and three times more feeding compared to females not so guarded.

intent on harassing them. But what benefits are to be gained by being guarded against such attacks? It may be that pheasants, whilst feeding on superabundant, low quality food such as growing shoots, face a 'digestive bottleneck' whereby their rate of energy assimilation depends not on their feeding rate but on their rate of digestion of food taken in. Pheasants generally have full stomachs and intestines at whatever time of day they are analysed, whereas their crops are not full for most of the time (Dalke 1937). This suggests that only intermittent feeding is required to supply continuous digestion, so that energy uptake is limited by digestion rate. Some grouse feeding on low quality but superabundant pine needles experience the same situation (Wittenberger 1978). Therefore, if food is abundant, the energy balance of a pheasant is determined by the rate at which it expends energy subtracted from a relatively inflexible rate of uptake (Sibley 1981).

Consequently the energy spent by a female escaping from a harassing, non-territorial male intent on raping her cannot be recouped by more feeding, but is subtracted from the amount otherwise destined for egg formation. Flying is about 15 times as energetically costly as basal metabolism (the basic rate of energy expenditure of a resting bird), whereas walking is no more than 1–2 times as costly (King 1974). Running falls somewhere between the two. Therefore female pheasants reduce the energy expenditure of escaping from harassing males by living in a harem that is guarded by a territorial male. Mate guarding therefore protects females not only from the physical risks of rape, predation or injury, but also from excessive energy expenditure. This is something that can be as easily provided to a small group of females as to one.

By associating with one particular male who has demonstrated through his displays that he is the undisputed dominant within that area, females gain a companion who not only remains vigilant while they feed, but who also keeps other males at bay. Mate guarding in this way is common in conspicuous species which feed in the open such as magpies (Birkhead 1979), mallard (Barash, 1978), pintails (Wishart and Knapton 1978), and some of the few harem-defending birds such as rheas (Bruning 1974), combe ducks (Siegfried 1978) and red junglefowl (McBride *et al.* 1969).

During nesting and brood rearing the hens are secretive to avoid the attentions of predators. The male takes no part in nest building, incubation or brood rearing and his presence during these periods would not necessarily be an advantage. As such all that the male provides for the females is that he stands guard while they feed and allows them to build up large body reserves. Mate guarding is expensive for the male, as he must stop feeding and deter intruders. However, this is something that need only be provided for one or two hours per day when the hens are in the open; when in cover they are safe from disturbance. If the females had to be guarded 24 hours a day, as is the case for species that permanently live in the open, then the male might not be able to provide such protection for more than one hen. Nevertheless, guarding for short periods of time is something that can just as efficiently be provided for a dozen hens as for one. There is no disadvantage to a hen in breeding with a cock who already has other mates and so they are free to choose amongst all the males. Many hens may choose the same cock, giving rise to a polygynous mating system.

Territorial harem defence in pheasants resembles that in ungulate mammals, such as some species of deer, in several ways: females are gregarious and males territorial; female groups live mostly within one male's territory where the resident guards them and mates with them, and the association does not usually last until parturition or hatching. Pheasants are more like mammals than birds with respect to their breeding behaviour because by their gregarious, herbivorous, conspicuous habits and their reluctance to fly, females offer the same opportunities for harem guarding as in, for example, ungulates. By contrast polygyny in some passerine birds is organised on altogether different lines: they are inconspicuous, fast-moving (in three dimensions), and solitary targets for an intruding male. Mate guarding is therefore found only in conspicuous monogamous birds and a few large, ground-dwelling polygynous ones such as the pheasant.

5 Clutches

Mate guarding by the male continues as the females gather food resources in order to prepare for breeding. Females tend to move longer distances in successive days until they find a place in which to lay their clutch. The nest is usually a scrape amongst leaves or residual vegetation, sometimes lined with roots and the occasional feather, but nests have also been recorded in trees, old nests of other birds and in squirrel dreys.

Pheasants lay a large number of eggs, typically up to 15 for first nesting attempts, although more have been recorded. The Game Conservancy's Pheasant Nest Recording Scheme (PNRS) and data from the British Trust for Ornithology's Nest Recording Scheme (BTO) indicate an average clutch of 11.4 eggs. There are physiological constraints associated with laying such a large number of eggs, which for the pheasant represents 40% of its body weight. The condition of the female may be important in the clutch's success and in her ability to incubate it properly, or in her ability to produce another clutch if the first one fails. The timing of laying can be crucial to the subsequent survival of chicks which depend on an insect-rich food supply. The spring and summer breeding periods are of course important to the success of the subsequent shooting season and consequently a great deal of work has been done internationally on factors affecting pheasant breeding performance and productivity in the wild.

SELECTING A PLACE TO NEST

Before the advent of radiotelemetry, female pheasants in Britain were thought always to nest in woodlands in preference to other habitats. Their secrecy at this time of year precluded their nests being found in the more difficult to search cereal crops. Studies in the corn growing belt of the United States where small woodlots were the only such habitats available to pheasants did show that these birds nested mainly in cereal fields and other farm crops but preferences, based on the areas of these habitats, were rarely established. By following females equipped with radiotransmitters it has been possible to find out which habitats pheasants prefer; invaluable information if they are to be managed.

Our radiomarked females have shown a distinct preference for nesting in woodland early in the breeding season, particularly April and May. By June, however, the proportion of nests started in woodlands declined and that in cereal crops, which had now achieved reasonable height, increased (Fig. 5.1). Birds were found nesting more than 200 metres from the nearest woodland-field boundary within winter wheat and winter barley. Taken throughout the breeding season, tall herbaceous cover is preferred to woodland habitat. This seasonal change in habitat preference has not previously been documented by either of the nest recording schemes mentioned earlier, presumably because both data sets are biased towards early nests and few people search

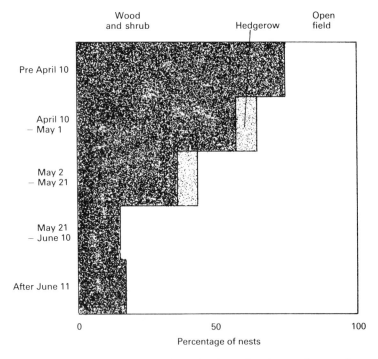

Fig. 5.1 Seasonal changes in nest-site selection, showing preference for woodland and shrubs early on and for cereal fields later in the season.

large areas of cereal fields, preferring to look in woods where
they expect to find them.

We reanalysed the data of five detailed studies conducted in
the United States, in which nest searches were carried out across
all habitat types. On reanalysis using a standard technique to
determine preference or avoidance (Neu, Byers and Peek 1974),
some similarities in selection were uncovered (Table 5.1). In all
cases alfalfa, or vegetation at roadsides, was the preferred nesting
habitat, as to a lesser extent were fencerows and edges of two
adjoining habitats. In these studies, cereal fields and pastures
were avoided, although by nature of their sheer size it is doubtful
whether female pheasants would ever venture far into some of
the large expenses of corn.

That some habitats are selected on the basis of their vegetation
does not necessarily mean the nests have a higher chance of
success. Nesting in alfalfa, for example, certainly represents a

Table 5.1 Selection of nest-sites and the proportion successful in different habitats based on five studies from the literature

Habitat	Prop. of area	Nest density (no./ha)	Prop. of nests	Prop. of successful nests
(a)				
Fence and ditch	0.03	2.11	0.35^{+**}	0.26^{+*}
Hay and alfalfa	0.18	0.33	0.31^{+*}	0.26^{ns}
Cereal	0.51	0.08	0.20^{-**}	0.44^{ns}
Pasture	0.21	0.05	0.06^{-**}	0^{-**}
Other	0.13	0.15	0.10^{ns}	0.04^{-*}
N	371 ha		72	27
(b)				
Roadsides	0.03	4.72	0.27^{+**}	0.25^{+**}
Wheat	0.60	0.49	0.24^{-**}	0.53^{-*}
Alfalfa	0.07	2.32	0.27^{+**}	0.03^{-*}
Abandoned farmland	0.08	1.36	0.09^{ns}	0.10^{ns}
Pasture and hay	0.21	1.06	0.11^{-**}	0.09^{-**}
Fencerow	0.01	1.56	0.02^{+**}	0^{ns}
N	1700 ha		1152	288
(c)				
Oats	0.26	1.12	0.16^{-**}	0.25^{ns}
Flax	0.13	0.54	0.04^{-**}	0.08^{-*}
Pasture	0.21	1.03	0.12^{-**}	0.15^{-*}
Alfalfa	0.12	3.68	0.24^{+**}	0.07^{-*}
Barley	0.06	1.69	0.05^{ns}	0.07^{ns}
Wheat	0.03	0.75	0.01^{-**}	0.04^{ns}
Hay	0.03	2.90	0.05^{ns}	0.06^{ns}
Roadsides and edges	0.06	7.03	0.21^{+**}	0.15^{+**}
Other	0.09	2.68	0.13^{+**}	0.13^{ns}
N	633 ha		1200	257
(d)				
Alfalfa	0.10	1.90	0.28^{+**}	0.07^{ns}
Wheat	0.72	0.37	0.38^{-**}	0.55^{-**}
Roadsides	0.04	4.12	0.24^{+**}	0.35^{+**}
Pastures	0.12	0.19	0.04^{-**}	0.02^{-**}
Fencerows	0.01	3.09	0.03^{+**}	0^{ns}
Other	0.01	1.77	0.03^{+**}	0.02^{ns}
N	1813 ha		880	133

(continued)

Table 5.1 Continued

Habitat	Prop. of area	Nest density (no./ha)	Prop. of nests	Prop. of successful nests
(e)				
Woods and ground veg.	0.31	26.5	0.50^{+**}	0.52^{+**}
Woods and no ground veg.	0.11	16.1	0.11^{ns}	0.11^{ns}
Ungrazed pasture	0.14	17.3	0.15^{ns}	0.154^{ns}
Grazed pasture	0.16	8.0	0.08^{-**}	0.07^{-**}
Abandoned farmland	0.03	40.1	0.06^{+**}	0.08^{+**}
Cereal	0.20	4.0	0.05^{-**}	0.04^{-**}
Hay and alfalfa	0.05	19.9	0.06^{ns}	0.03^{-*}
N	142 ha		2360	1075

Note: Preference and avoidance of different habitats was tested using the technique of Neu, Byers and Peek (1974), $*P<0.05$, $**P<0.001$, ^{ns} not significant.
(a) From Baskett (1941)
(b) From Baxter and Wolfe (1973)
(c) From Trautman (1960)
(d) From Linder *et al.* (1960)
(e) From Stokes (1954)

bad risk for pheasants as this crop is cut at a time when most nests are being incubated and many hens are either killed on the nest or, if they escape, their clutch is often lost. The cutting of alfalfa destroys many nests, and, generally, nests are significantly less successful in alfalfa than are those placed on roadsides and ditches (Table 5.1). In the Nebraska study 37% of nests were destroyed by farming operations, including 22% by the mowing of alfalfa. In addition the mowing caused the death of 14% of the spring female population.

A shift similar to that which we observed from woodland to the taller vegetation afforded by cereal fields has been found in the United States. Pheasants were found to change the position of replacement nests from old-fields, which provide the most cover in the early part of the breeding season, to hay, alfalfa and wheat crops in the later months. A number of studies have shown that female pheasants select their nest-site directly in relation to the quality of cover provided (Hanson 1970, Baxter and Wolfe 1973, Wood and Brotherson 1981). Damp or wet conditions are also avoided by nesting pheasants, and while cover is needed to protect the nest from predators, dense, rank cover can impede escape if the nest is approached by a mammalian predator such as a fox.

The number of nests per unit area varies between different habitats. From analysis of the data from the five American studies, nest density was highest in such habitats as fencerows, ditches, roadsides, alfalfa and hay meadows (Table 5.1). Pheasants on Pelee Island bred at the highest densities yet recorded, probably because of the abundance of suitable food, cover and the virtual absence of predators. Woods which had a shrubby ground layer of vegetation and abandoned farmland were the two habitats with the highest density of nests in the Pelee Island study. Pheasants nested at lower densities in woods lacking the shrubby vegetation, and ungrazed pastures with an abundance of shrubs held more nesting pheasants than pasture which was grazed and consequently had little ground vegetation (Table 5.1e). So the life-forms within a particular set of habitats are important factors influencing nesting density.

Bluebells growing on the floor of an old oak woodland with a hazel coppice understorey often provide good nesting cover for pheasants. Bluebells, by nature of their leafy growth using resources from last year's bulbs, provide a carpet of relatively tall cover early in the season whilst the tree canopy is still open enough for them to photosynthesise. Very dense ground vegetation is seldom used as a nest-site. Often a few bramble briars are all that are needed to protect the hen and break up her outline. Nests at the foot of a tree have the same effect. Indeed, we have observed hens sitting on nests at the base of trees within bare-ground Douglas fir plantations where the outline is sufficiently broken up to afford concealment.

Artificial nesting baskets have often been used to increase both nesting density and nest success of island breeding waterfowl, particularly those on ecologically immature flooded gravel quarries. However, this does not appear to work with pheasants (Russell 1974). Various structures have been tested in the USA with no success.

HOME RANGES OF LAYING FEMALES

Whilst the female is collecting food for laying she is still accompanied by her mate when feeding in the open, returning to the nest to lay, on average, one egg every 1.4 days. During this time she occupies what we generally recognise as her laying range which is often some distance from the position of her mate's territory. The average laying range for all nesting attempts in 18 radiotagged hens was 16.0 ± 2.9 ha, which was, on average, 9 ha smaller than the pre-nesting range, during which time females associate with males.

The size of the range during the laying of a renest clutch is generally smaller than that of the first nest. For six hens which were followed with radiotransmitters their first laying range averaged 17.8 ± 3.6 ha, whilst that of the second nest averaged 10.9 ± 4.0 ha.

There is generally no relationship between the size of pre-nesting ranges and the size of laying ranges. Whilst the two types of range often overlap, they tend to be separate entities with regard to size and possibly reflect differences in the exploitation of resources as the season progresses.

One particularly interesting finding from our radiomarked hens was that in 15 out of 24 laying ranges studied the nest was on the edge of the range (Fig. 5.2). This has important implications for predation. We might envisage that feeding away from the nest was beneficial to the clutch's chance of success if, for example, the predator was more likely to find the nest by using female activity close to it as a clue.

LAYING DATES AND THE NUMBERS OF EGGS

There are a number of factors which determine the date of laying by individual females and the number of eggs they will lay. These can be conveniently split into two categories—ultimate and proximate factors. Ultimate factors involved in determining laying date include the need to hatch chicks when food is most plentiful for them. For obvious reasons the breeding seasons of birds in temperate regions are, in part, geared towards producing chicks at a time when they are most likely to survive, i.e. when food supplies

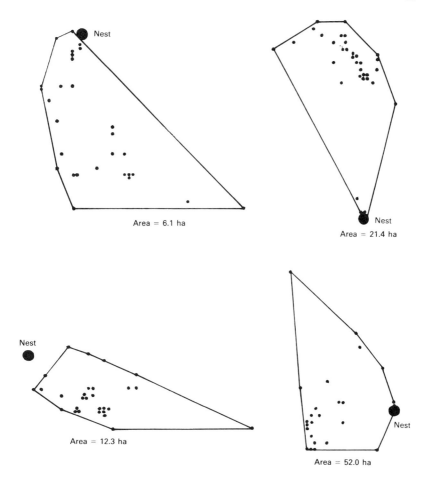

Fig. 5.2 Laying ranges of four radiotagged females showing that nests are generally placed at the edge of the range (not to scale).

are most abundant. Similarly, hens should not lay too many eggs as this could exhaust their reserves of fat, require a longer laying period with an increased risk of predation, and the hen may not be able to successfully incubate a large clutch or brood the resulting chicks.

Proximate factors influencing laying date and clutch size and which cause seasonal and individual variations are usually less obvious. In those bird species studied factors such as age, experience of the mate, body condition, habitat and weather play a role in determining laying date. Older individuals of most bird species

Plate VIII. The average pheasant clutch contains about 11 eggs. However, early clutches are often much larger. (*D.A. Hill*)

studied tend to lay eggs earlier than younger individuals, usually because older ones are heavier and in better condition. Bad weather such as low temperatures in early spring have also been demonstrated to delay laying in some species, and some evidence has shown that birds nesting in good quality habitats breed earlier. Body condition has also been shown to be an important determinant of the number of eggs laid by many species (Bengtson 1972, Batt and Prince 1979, Krapu 1979, Dijkstra *et al.* 1982). Continued winter feeding after the shooting season can make a difference to the condition in which the birds enter the breeding season, and may aid successful breeding.

Indeed, significant delays in egg laying in pheasants have been shown, but only under experimental conditions, to be associated with poor nutrition (Breitenbach *et al.* 1965). Following severe winters, although no instances of outright starvation were recorded, Gates and Woehler (1968) showed that hens suffered a depletion of body reserves when they should have been gaining weight in preparation for reproduction. There is also some evidence that laying date is delayed in cool wet springs (Buss and Swanson

1950, Baxter and Wolfe 1973), although studies of radiotagged birds have shown little seasonal variation.

Records of pheasant nests obtained from nest recording schemes (BTO and PNRS) and our own data obtained from following radiotagged females indicate that the first eggs are usually laid in early April and that laying continues throughout the summer and even until September. The average dates on which the first eggs were laid in those nests found in the PNRS and BTO schemes were 19 and 24 April ($\pm$ 0.7 days in each case) respectively (Fig. 5.3). This was significantly earlier than for the unbiased sample of nests found by radiotelemetry with a mean first egg date of 22 May. Casual observers tend to miss late nests together with those located within cereal fields.

Generally, pheasants lay an average of 10–12 eggs. Incubated clutches from the three data sources, i.e. PNRS, BTO and radio-telemetry, contained an average of 11.4 $\pm$ 0.1 eggs (n=1384 clutches), and maximum clutch size was 28 eggs, although some even larger ones, including one of 34 eggs, were found but not incubated (Fig. 5.4).

With the exception of a few reports of male pheasants being observed on nests, incubation is conducted entirely by the female. The reports of incubating males may be misleading. One physiological abnormality that occurs with some frequency is that of hens developing male plumage. It is not uncommon to find hens with spurs, some male feathers or, in the more extreme cases, complete male plumages with the exception of wattles and pinnae. These androgenous hens appear to result from a malfunction of the ovaries and subsequent disruption of hormone production. Some of these birds can still produce eggs and this has undoubtedly been the explanation for some of the reports of male pheasants incubating a clutch. Of some 3000 shot birds examined we found three such instances. There are also reports of captive males incubating clutches. These are often associated with injured birds and may again reflect disruption of normal hormonal activity.

Mean clutch size has been shown to decline through the season (Fig. 5.5). This may be related to the increased laying period needed to lay larger clutches and the need to hatch broods relatively early in the season when insect abundance is high. Also renest clutches tend to contain fewer eggs than first nests.

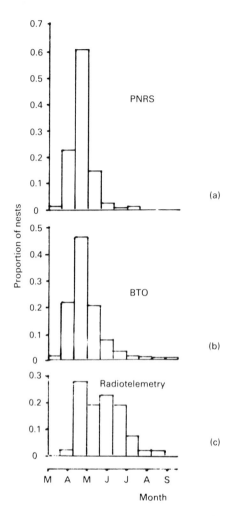

Fig. 5.3 The distribution of laying dates in pheasants from three sources, (a) the Pheasant Nest Recording Scheme, (b) the British Trust for Ornithology's Nest Record Scheme, and (c) from radiotagged hens.

It is possible to determine how many eggs a hen can effectively incubate by looking at the hatchability of eggs from clutches of different sizes. There were surprising similarities in the physical limit of effective clutch size between data provided by Stokes' (1954) Pelee Island study and the PNRS and BTO data in Britain. As the clutch size of a particular nest increased so the number of chicks hatched from it increased, but only to a certain point–20 eggs in our data and 23 eggs in the Pelee Island study (Fig. 5.6).

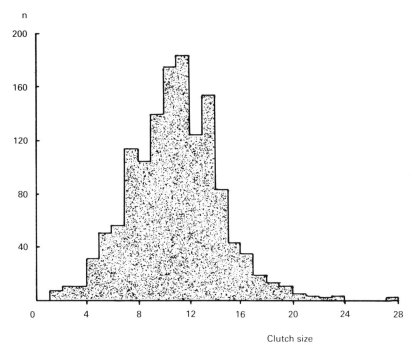

Fig. 5.4 Clutch size distribution of incubated nests, data from three sources combined.

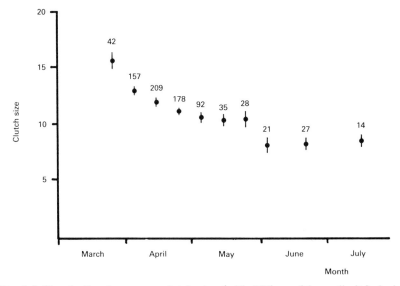

Fig. 5.5 The decline in average clutch size (with 95% confidence limits) during the breeding season. Data from the three sources combined, with number of clutches shown above points.

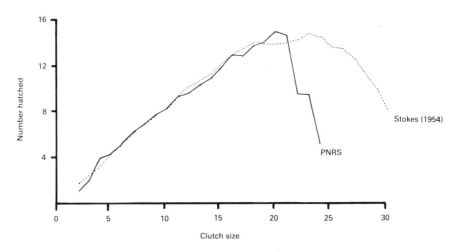

Fig. 5.6 The number of eggs hatched from clutches of increasing size from the PNRS and as calculated from Stokes (1954).

In terms of the percentage hatched there were significant declines as clutch size increased beyond about 12 eggs. In clutches of 21 eggs in both studies, less than 70% would be expected to hatch (Fig. 5.7). Beyond 21 eggs there were dramatic declines in hatchability.

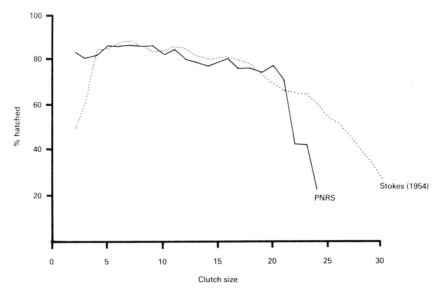

Fig. 5.7 The proportion of eggs hatched from clutches of increasing size from the PNRS and as calculated from Stokes (1954).

It has been shown for some species of ducks that egg quality can effect the subsequent survival of the young. Consequently large eggs with large fat reserves are better than smaller eggs which provide the chick with fewer resources. Faced with the dilemma of laying fewer large eggs or a large number of small ones, what should pheasants do?

For females given free access to food in captivity, average egg weight has been found to be remarkably constant irrespective of female age and time of laying (Labinsky and Jackson 1969). However, hens fed on limited diets have been shown to produce fewer eggs but of the same quality as a control group with free access to food (Breitenbach et al. 1965). Yearling females have been shown to produce significantly fewer eggs than adults under conditions when food was not a limiting factor (Labinsky and Jackson 1969), due largely to 2-year-olds having a longer laying period, beginning laying earlier and ending later. Females which weigh less at the end of the winter tend to begin egg laying at progressively lower weights in spring. This can have implications for survival during the summer when stress resistance is at its lowest ebb following the high energy demands for egg laying, incubation and care of young. Indeed Wagner (1957) showed that survival after nesting was lower in females of low weight the previous spring.

In conclusion then, females appear to sacrifice their own body condition and possibly their survival prospects in order to ensure the production of good quality eggs. When food is in short supply during the period prior to nesting they may lay fewer eggs, but their quality remains the same.

DUMPING EGGS IN THE NESTS OF OTHERS

In a number of bird species, including pheasants, some individuals 'dump' eggs in the nests of other members of the population. This is often prevalent when birds nest at a high density and this is certainly true of pheasants (Allen 1956). It is thought to be a strategy for enhancing one's own contribution to the population without investing time in incubation and experiencing the associated risks, such as predation.

Generally, dump nesting is identified when more than one egg is laid in a nest per day, indicating that two or more females are

using it. We looked at the BTO and PNRS data in order to find
out more about dump nesting, when it occurs, and to postulate
the advantages and disadvantages of it to individual birds, be
they dumping females or hosts.

We used these data to calculate the probabilities of certain
events happening during the laying period, in relation to increasing
clutch size. As clutch size increased to 15 eggs the probability of
another egg being laid in the nest declined, but then, beyond this
point, it increased and peaked at 21 eggs, before declining with
larger clutch sizes (Fig. 5.8a). This 'blip' in the data is apparently
caused by 'dumping females'. The probability of a nest being
abandoned was relatively low for clutches containing fewer than
15 eggs but then began to rise steeply as clutch size increased
(Fig. 5.8b). Abandonment of clutches rose from 10% of those
containing 21 eggs to 50% of those containing more than 24.
Therefore, a small difference in the number of eggs laid gave rise
to a large difference in the chance of the clutch being abandoned.
This abandonment may well be due to greater interference caused
to the host female by other females intent on laying their eggs in
her nest.

The probability of a clutch being incubated, and consequently
of the hen terminating egg laying, increased as clutch size reached
12 but declined for larger clutches (Fig. 5.8c). The probability of
any other loss was not obviously related to clutch size (Fig. 5.8d).

By assuming that the probability of a hen laying another egg in
her own nest declines steadily, based on an inverse logistic curve
extrapolated from the first 10 data points, it is possible to predict
the probability of a nest containing a dumped egg with increasing
clutch size (Fig. 5.8a). As shown, this probability increases after
15 eggs have already been laid in the nest and in the larger
clutches of over 20 eggs it was actually more likely for the next
egg to be laid by a dumping female than by the owner of the nest.
This analysis suggests that 1–2% of eggs are laid into other
females' nests but that 7% of nests are parasitised to some extent.

We have never observed radiotagged pheasants laying in
incubated clutches whilst the owner has been off feeding, so
dumping almost invariably occurs during the laying period. In
fact, there seems little advantage in dumping an egg into a clutch
already partly incubated as the dumped egg will not hatch. We do

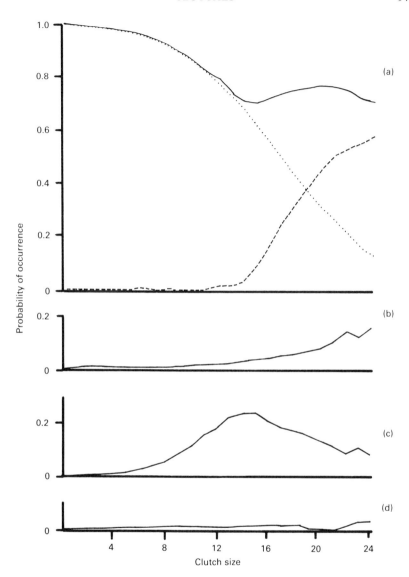

Fig. 5.8 The probability during any stage of the laying period of (a) another egg occurring in the nest (the blip shows the contribution made by hens dumping eggs in the nests of other hens), (b) the nest being abandoned, (c) the nest being incubated successfully, (d) any other loss, in relation to an increasing number of eggs being laid.

not yet know whether 'parasitic' females have their own nest at the same time as they are dumping eggs in the nests of others.

Research in the USA has shown that females will sometimes shift their range and begin incubating existing clutches containing 8 to 18 eggs, after only 4 to 6 days in the new area. Other work has shown this promiscuous laying and adoption of nests to be much less common (Gates 1971) and to be greater under conditions of high breeding density (Dumke and Pils 1979).

Pheasants have also been reported to dump eggs in the nests of other bird species including grey and red-legged partridges (Potts 1986), woodcock, various duck species (McAttee 1945, Baxter and Wolfe 1973) and corncrake (Cramp and Simmons 1980). On a radiotracking site in Dorset we observed two hens taking turns to incubate one clutch which successfully hatched, while females have also been observed side by side incubating a dump nest together. Indeed, up to four hens sitting on one nest has been recorded for penned birds, and in the same study, when any one female left these large dump nests, adjacent incubating birds helped themselves to some of her eggs, thereby increasing the size of their clutch (Breitenbach et al. 1965). Sometimes, the behaviour of hand-reared pheasants defies explanation!

MOVEMENTS AND BEHAVIOUR DURING THE INCUBATION PERIOD

Female pheasants do not cover their eggs when they leave the nest to feed during the incubation period. Females must therefore feed relatively quickly and return to the nest as soon as possible before the eggs become chilled. Females have been found to leave the nest between 26 and 46 times during the 25—day incubation period, mostly between 0700 and 0900 hours and 1600 and 1800 hours. They spend more time off the nest during the earlier and later stages of incubation than during the intermediate period (Kessler 1962, Kuck et al. 1970).

Whilst females often allow the approach of other individuals near to the nest, particularly when housed in pens, their aggressiveness to intruders increases as incubation progresses (Breitenbach et al. 1965). In this study there was marked variation in aggression between different females, which could well influence their vulnerability to predation during incubation. Interestingly, the BTO

nest records include two cases where dead stoats were found next
to pheasant nests. We wonder whether this was as a result of nest
defence by the incubating hen?

Earlier we showed that the female generally places her nest on
the edge of the range she occupies during the laying period. This,
we suggest, is a strategy to reduce the risks of predation to both
herself and her clutch, based on the probable increased likelihood
of being detected in relation to activity close to the nest site.
During feeding bouts throughout the incubation period our radiotracking data support the idea that the female continues to maintain this apparent avoidance of the nest-site area. We located
them feeding further than 50 metres from the nest, significantly
more than if they had fed randomly. Indeed in periods away from
the nest during incubation hens were observed feeding most often
at between 50 and 150 metres from the nest, the area up to 50
metres radius from the nest being less used (Fig. 5.9).

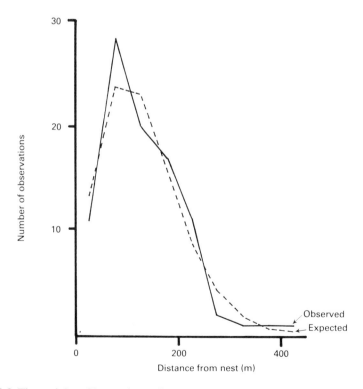

Fig. 5.9 The activity of hens when off the nest in relation to the distance from it.

PREDATION DURING NESTING

Female pheasants are cryptically coloured as they must incubate a clutch of eggs in relatively open conditions, particularly during the early part of the breeding season when vegetation will not have reached its greatest height. This plumage presumably reduces the likelihood of being seen at a time when they are particularly vulnerable to predation. However, foxes usually hunt by scent, their eyesight being much less impressive, as anyone who uses dogs to 'pickup" pheasants during a day's shooting will testify. The sense of smell of mammalian predators is usually well-developed, and many, such as the fox, use it both to locate food and to communicate using territorial scent marking. Adaptations by ground-nesting birds to reduce detection would be expected to be equally well developed. There is a general belief that females of many ground nesting species reduce their scent output during incubation, either because of a general reduction of activity or because of a more active suppression of scent production. Hudson (1986) has neatly shown that pointing-dogs locate a greater proportion of parasitised as opposed to unparasitised red grouse than one would expect if they were finding birds at random. He suggests the reason may be due to the effect of the parasites on the control of scent emission by female grouse. Certainly birds carrying large burdens of the parasitic worm *Trichostrongylus tenuis* have larger caeca and it is possible that these parasites interfere with the control of the caecum and potential scent emissions. In this instance, Hudson found that vulnerability to predation, presumably as a consequence of the interference of scent control, was higher in grouse infected with parasites than in birds dosed with an anthelmintic drug which removed the worms. Another possible reason for greater predation on infected birds is that the parasites compete for the hen's reserves during incubation, forcing them to leave the nest and feed more frequently than uninfected hens. The increased activity could again result in more scent being left near the nests of heavily parasitised hens.

Pheasant clutches succumb to predators during both the laying period and incubation. Information from six published studies is presented in Table 5.2, together with data from our radiomarked birds. Nest success varied dramatically between localities—in these

Table 5.2 Summary of nest losses and cause of loss, from the literature

	Baskett (1941)	Trautman (1960)	Snyder (1984)*	Linder et al. (1960)	Snyder (1974)	Baxter & Wolfe (1973)	This study Damerham & Lyons *
Total nests observed	72	1200	105	880	170	1032	57
Total nests lost	45	943	52	747	130	925	35
Nest success (%)	38	21	51	15	24	10	39
Predation (%) fox (%)	18 (25)		21 (20)	218 (25)	93 (55)	586 (57)	19 (33)
other	0 (0)						10 (18)
mammal (%)	16 (22)			203 (23)			
bird (%)	2 (3)			15 (2)			9 (16)
agricultural disturbance	15 (21)		27 (26)	327 (37)			5 (9)
Other losses (%)	1 (1)		0 (0)	96 (11)	18 (11)	178 (17)	4 (7)
Abandoned (%)	11(15)		4 (4)	106 (12)	19 (11)	161 (16)	7 (12)

Note: * Refers to radiomarked birds in the study concerned.

studies from 10.4% to 50.5%, the variation being largely attributable to variation in the proportion of clutches destroyed by predators. Agricultural disturbances, as we have said previously,
appeared to account for a large proportion of clutches in some
studies whilst abandonment rates were also high in others, particularly that of Stokes on Pelee Island where nest density was
the highest yet recorded (up to 40 nests per hectare).

In Britain, carrion or hooded crows and magpies are the major
predators of eggs during the laying period while mammals such as
foxes, hedgehogs and badgers are also important. Grey partridge
nests are also particularly vulnerable to hedgehogs because the
nest is usually situated at the base of a hedge, often a corridor of
activity for these mammals (Potts 1986).

The Pheasant Nest Recording Scheme was conducted by gamekeepers and they were often able to identify the predator involved
when any eggs were predated. Calculating the daily rates of nest
loss from these data (Mayfield 1961, Hensler and Nichols 1981)
(Table 5.3) we found that avian predators destroyed three times
as many clutches during the laying period compared with during
incubation, which is to be expected as the nest is more exposed
during laying than during incubation when it is covered by the
hen. We know of no records, for example, of corvids attempting
to remove the sitting hen from the nest. Abandonment, as we
have seen, was particularly high during laying. Overall it accounted
for the loss of 17% of all clutches recorded in the PNRS.

The losses of nests attributed to various causes were similar for
the PNRS scheme and our radiotagged birds (Table 5.4). Abandonment accounted for the loss of 13% of clutches of radiomarked
hens during incubation compared with 8.2% from the PNRS
data, but losses from agricultural disturbances were higher for
nests of radiomarked birds. In terms of contributions to total
losses there were marked similarities. For example, foxes taking
hens on the nest during incubation accounted for 13.3% of total
nest losses in the PNRS and 15.6% of those from radiomarked
hens. Furthermore corvids accounted for 13.3% of total nest
losses in the PNRS and 18.7% of those from radiomarked hens.
During incubation foxes accounted for 37.8% of all nest losses in
the PNRS and 31.2% of those from hens carrying radios.

The 54 hens that we radiotagged and followed were nesting on
unkeepered estates. The information from the BTO scheme also

Table 5.3 Causes of loss of 280 nests during laying and 354 nests during incubation from the Pheasant Nest Recording Scheme, together with causes of loss of 54 nests from radiotagged females during incubation

| | Pheasant Nest Recording Scheme | | | | | | Radiotagged females | | |
| | Laying | | | Incubation | | | Incubation | | |
	no.	% total	% of losses	no.	% total	% of losses	no.	% total	% of losses
Hedgehog	3	1.1	2.0	3	0.8	3.1	1	1.8	3.1
Dog	1	0.3	0.7	4	1.1	4.1	0	–	–
Cat	0	–	–	2	0.6	2.0	0	–	–
Fox	3	1.1	2.0	24	6.8	24.5	5	9.2	15.6
Corvid	35	12.5	23.8	13	3.7	13.3	6	11.1	18.7
Badger	0	–	–	2	0.6	2.0	1	1.8	3.1
Unknown	2	0.7	1.4	1	0.3	1.0	1	1.8	3.1
Abandoned	78	27.8	53.1	29	8.2	29.6	7	13.0	21.9
Agricultural	12	4.3	8.2	2	0.6	2.0	5	9.2	15.6
Other predator	9	3.2	6.1	2	0.6	2.0	1	1.8	3.1
Dog (hen)	2	0.7	1.4	1	0.3	1.0	0	–	–
Fox (hen)	2	0.7	1.4	13	3.7	13.3	5	9.2	15.6
Cat (hen)	0	–	–	2	0.6	2.0	0	–	–
Total lost	147	52.5	100	98	27.7	100	32	59.2	100
Total nests	280			354			54		

Table 5.4 Daily nest survival rates with 95% confidence limits using the Mayfield method for estimating nest success during the laying and incubation periods of the Pheasant Nest Recording Scheme (PNRS), and the incubation period of radio-tagged females: Number in parentheses

	PNRS		Radiotagged females
	Laying	Incubation	Incubation
Loss of eggs to predator *	0.969 ± 0.008 (51)	0.991 ± 0.002 (50)	0.984 ± 0.008 (14)
Mammal (ns)	0.990 ± 0.005 (16)	0.993 ± 0.002 (37)	0.991 ± 0.006 (8)
Bird *	0.979 ± 0.007 (35)	0.998 ± 0.001 (13)	0.993 ± 0.006 (6)
Abandoned *	0.953 ± 0.010 (78)	0.995 ± 0.002 (29)	0.992 ± 0.006 (7)
Loss of hen and eggs to predator (ns)	0.998 ± 0.002 (4)	0.997 ± 0.001 (16)	0.994 ± 0.005 (5)
Overall daily survival rate (%) (a)	0.912 ± 0.014 (47.5)	0.983 ± 0.003 (72.3)	0.963 ± 0.013 (b) (40.8)
Number of bird days	1676	5654	871

Note:
* Difference in laying and incubation periods for PNRS, $P<0.001$
(ns) Not significant
(a) In PNRS data nest survival was lower during laying than during incubation ($z=9.97$, $P<0.001$)
(b) Overall daily survival rate during incubation was higher for the PNRS data than for that from radio-tagged birds ($z=3.03$, $P<0.005$).

came largely from unkeepered areas, collected in a casual manner. In contrast the information in the PNRS was collected entirely by gamekeepers as they walked round their beats. The information can therefore be split into keepered and unkeepered categories and compared in order to see whether gamekeeping reduced nest losses during incubation. We have little information from radio-marked females for the laying period as it is not always possible to tell by radiotelemetry if a hen is laying a clutch without getting so close as to risk disturbing her during this sensitive period. Using the Mayfield technique to convert losses attributable to various causes into daily rates of loss we found that there was an interesting, but not entirely unexpected difference. The daily survival rate of nests during incubation from radiomarked birds and nests in the BTO scheme were significantly lower than that of nests from the keepered estates, representing overall losses during incubation of 61%, 51% and 35% respectively (Table 5.5). Consequently it would appear that the predator control carried out on those estates contributing to the PNRS had a significant effect of increasing the survival of clutches during both laying and incubation.

The dynamics of predation on gamebirds is still poorly understood, although Potts (1986) has shown that the proportion of clutches and incubating hens of the grey partridge which are destroyed by predators increases as the density of nesting birds increases, but this effect can be removed by the action of a gamekeeper. This may also be true of pheasants but there is as yet little direct evidence.

Table 5.5 Estimated daily rates of nest survival ($P \pm 95\%$ confidence limits) of pheasant nests during laying and incubation determined from PNRS data, BTO data and nests of radiomarked females

Source of data	PNRS	BTO	Radiotelemetry
(a) Laying	0.912 ± 0.014	0.899 ± 0.014	–
(nest days)	1676	1769	–
(b) Incubation	0.983 ± 0.003	0.972 ± 0.004	0.963 ± 0.012
(nest days)	5654	7461	871

RENESTING

One advantage of early nesting is that females which lose a clutch can start another nest. Although the production of eggs is a large investment on the part of the hen, the size of the first clutch does not appear to influence the size of the second. We compiled data on the size of first and second clutches of 69 marked females from six studies in the literature, together with our own work, and found no relationship between the two (Fig. 5.10).

Some females make up to four nesting attempts in any one year (Dumke and Pils 1979), and generally more than 60% of females which lose their first clutch will attempt a second. Because of the regression of the ovaries after laying it takes longer for a female to produce a renest clutch if she has been incubating for some time than for a female that loses her clutch early in incubation.

Females can and do renest after loss of their brood. This is very much less common than replacing a clutch lost during laying or incubation, because of the greater amount of energy expended by the time the brood is lost. In a study in Wisconsin in the USA 4 out of 74 radiotagged females laid a repeat clutch after early loss of the brood (Dumke and Pils 1979), whilst 3 of 12 radiomarked hens did so in a study in New York (Penrod *et al.* 1982).

Unsuccessful females move variable distances between their

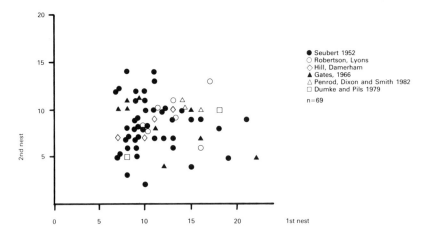

Fig. 5.10 There is generally no relationship between the number of eggs in the female's first clutch and the number in a replacement clutch. Data from six sources in the literature.

Table 5.6 Distances between successive nests of radiomarked female pheasants

Mean distance	Range	n	Source
396	63–2264	46	Dumke and Pils 1979
164	149–178	2	Kuck *et al.* 1970
370	–	11	Gates 1966
214	41–573	13	Robertson 1986
249	64–683	6	Hill 1984

first and subsequent nesting attempts (Table 5.6), and will often change the type of vegetation in which successive nests are made.

There has been considerable debate as to whether hen pheasants can successfully rear two broods within one summer. Although there is no doubt that hens will lay again after the loss of a nest, or even a brood of young chicks, there is no evidence of hens attempting a second brood after successfully rearing their first, in either Europe or North America. It takes a hen 95 days to lay ten

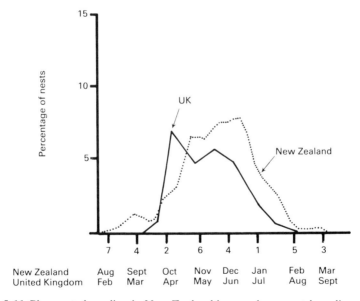

Fig. 5.11 Pheasants breeding in New Zealand have a drawn-out breeding season because of the mildness of the climate, whereas those in Britain (from our radiomarked hens) breed over a more restricted period. (New Zealand data from Westerskov 1956.)

eggs, incubate them and rear the chicks to eight weeks of age. The short summers in most areas of the pheasant's range do not allow for this to occur twice.

However, in New Zealand, the mild climatic conditions provide one of the longest breeding seasons encountered by this species (Fig. 5.11). Westerskov (1956) records a number of cases of New Zealand hens rearing two broods to fledging although, even in such favourable circumstances, it is still unusual.

New Zealand pheasants appear to be peculiar in another way. In Europe and North America the hen rears the brood without any help from the cock and males seen escorting broods are exceptional. However, in New Zealand, Westerskov (1956) reports that 8% of broods were accompanied by both a cock and a hen. As the chicks feed themselves and it is unlikely that the mild climate of New Zealand creates a need for extra brooding of the chicks, it is difficult to see any advantage to the hen and chicks of having a male in attendance. One possible explanation is that the males are chaperoning the hens in the hope of fathering a subsequent brood should the hen lose her own or be able to rear a second. Such chaperoning by the males may only be profitable in areas experiencing an extended breeding season and does not seem to be a common phenomenon in the Northern Hemisphere.

6 Broods

The pheasant appears to have adapted so well to the lowland arable scene in Western Europe that we have often taken it for granted. Yet the grey partridge, which relies on similar habitats in summer, has suffered dramatic declines in most areas, mostly due to low chick survival resulting from changing agriculture. Hand-rearing has masked many changes in the ecology of truly wild pheasants and the survival of wild chicks has received less attention than with the partridge, largely because shoots can compensate for poor chick survival by releasing more poults, something which, until recently, was not practical for partridges.

HABITAT AND SURVIVAL OF CHICKS

Despite rearing, the numbers shot annually often fluctuate to reflect the survival of chicks the previous summer (Fig. 6.1). Chick survival is a particularly important area for research, both because of its consequences for the annual bag and also because poor chick survival has been held responsible for the dramatic declines in the numbers of grey partridges (see Potts 1970, 1980 for detailed reasoning).

In some early studies, gamebird chick diet was determined by killing a sample of chicks and analysing their crop contents under a microscope. It was therefore impossible to directly relate diet to chick survival. However, with the advent and widespread use of radiotelemetry it has been possible to investigate this part of the pheasant life cycle in much greater detail.

Hen pheasants fitted with small radiotransmitters were tracked throughout the spring in order to locate their nests. Approximately 25 days after the start of incubation the eggs hatch and, once dry, the chicks leave the nest. The hen leads the chicks to suitable feeding areas where the chicks begin to feed themselves. During early life the chicks cannot maintain their own body temperature

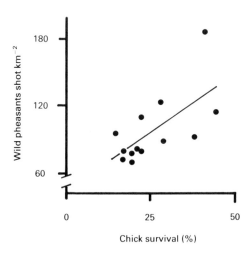

Fig. 6.1 The number of wild pheasants shot depends on how good the survival of chicks has been that year. This shows the relationship for the North Farm study area over the period 1970–1982.

Plate IX. A chick's eye view of a cereal field. (*D.A. Hill*)

and are periodically brooded by the hen to prevent them becoming chilled. This is particularly important during cold or wet
weather. The hen also warns the chicks of approaching danger
and on occasion they have been seen giving 'broken wing' dis-
traction displays to draw potential predators away from the chicks.
The hen calls to the chicks, starting even when they are still in
the egg. Once hatched the hen warns her brood of approaching
danger with a low−pitched call causing the chicks to scatter and
then freeze. After the threat has passed the hen gathers the brood
back together with another clucking call. Chicks give content-
ment calls and a more hurried caution call when disturbed. Solitary
chicks give another, plaintive call which attracts the hen and
other lost chicks to them.

Hens are very secretive when with their broods and radiotelemetry is the only way to determine the size of brood feeding
ranges, which habitats they use and what the chicks are feeding
upon. To do just this, we followed the movements of a number of
broods by locating the radiotagged hen. Furthermore, each night
during the first three weeks after the chicks hatched, we located

Plate X. By radiotracking it is possible to find the roost sites of young broods and collect their droppings for analysis. A large female dropping is shown, together with some from the chicks. (*D.A. Hill*)

the positions of their nocturnal roosts by triangulation and indicated the position with canes. On a subsequent visit the following morning we relocated this roost site and collected and counted the droppings left by the chicks and their mother for analysis in the laboratory. The lack of small droppings at the roost indicated that all chicks in a brood had died.

Changes in the volume of droppings left at nocturnal roosts suggest that, as in precocial chicks of many other species, most mortality occurs during the first 10–12 days after hatching. By locating, flushing and counting chicks at 3–4 weeks of age survival can be assessed and related to the size of the brood's range, the arthropods (especially insects) available to them, and their diet.

To determine the diet of the chicks, the faecal samples collected from the roosts were broken up in water and washed through a fine sieve. The droppings were viewed under a microscope and the remains of any arthropods assigned to species or group by identifying structures such as mandibles, labra, wings, tibiae, tarsi, elytra and eyes which are not digested and pass straight through the chick's digestive system. This technique has been used previously by Green (1984) for red-legged and grey partridges, and is described in detail by Moreby (in press).

Food supplies available within each brood's home range were also sampled by using a sweep net or a vacuum net sampler. These other methods in conjunction with radiotelemetry enable us to determine the brood's rate of survival, the size of its feeding range, the diet of the chicks, and the arthropods available to them.

Broods appear to move evenly within their selected habitat during the first three weeks of life and the average (with standard error) distance moved between successive nocturnal roosts was found to be 75 ±13 metres. The average size of the home range during the first ten days of life in the Damerham study was 4.8 ±1.0 ha which compares with 5–10 ha for broods tracked in Illinois (Warner 1979), and with two studies conducted in South Dakota, 2–4 ha (Kuck, Dahlgren and Progulske 1970) and 11 ha (Hanson and Progulske 1973). The size of the broods' home range has also been shown to increase as the chicks grow (Warner 1979) (Fig. 6.2).

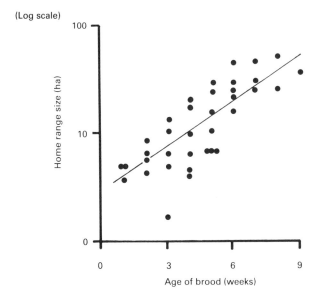

Fig. 6.2 The home range of a brood increases quickly in size during the first few weeks after leaving the nest. (Redrawn from Warner 1979.)

The survival rate of pheasant chicks from our radiotagged broods ranged from 0% to 88% of the brood. Those broods with the largest home ranges tended to suffer the highest mortality; similarly the larger ranges tended to contain lower densities of insects (Fig. 6.3). We conclude that broods which are short of food range over large areas and suffer heavier mortality. Warner (1984) also found that brood movements were much greater and ranges larger in broods feeding in large monoculture blocks than in those feeding within a more diverse complex of farming where insect densities would be expected to be higher.

Chicks belonging to our radiotagged hen pheasants ate arthropods of no fewer than 22 groups (Table 6.1). In terms of dry weight, plant hoppers (*Delphacidae*) and plant bugs (*Heteroptera*) together with the caterpillars of sawflies and *Lepidoptera*, made up 58% of the diet, the latter two types being highly favoured.

As the chicks grow their diet changes to one favouring plant material and seeds, particularly of *Agrostis* sp. and *Poa annua*

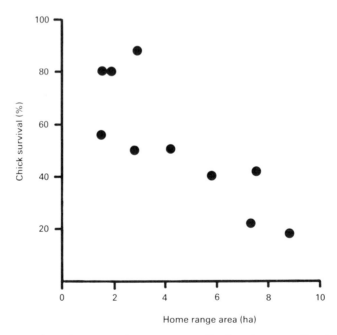

Fig. 6.3 Broods with a large home range suffer heavier mortality than those which stay within a small area. This is related to the amount of food available to chicks.

Table 6.1 Composition by dry weight (%) of the arthropod component of the diet of pheasant chicks (seven broods) as determined from the microscopic analysis of remains in faeces collected at nocturnal roost sites. The 'selection index' is calculated as % items in the diet divided by that of arthropod samples taken from the home range of broods

Food item	% in diet	Selection index
Araneida	2.3	0.2
Aphididae	8.1	1.8
Cicadellidae	4.1	0.3
Delphacidae	10.4	1.3
Heteroptera	17.5	0.7
Sawfly adult	0.1	1.0
Sawfly larvae	18.6	4.0
Lepidoptera larvae	11.6	8.9
Ichneumonidae	0.7	2.3
Braconidae	1.1	0.4
Formicidae	0.7	7.0
Carabidae adults	2.3	2.9
Carabidae larvae	0.4	4.0
Staphylinidae adults	1.0	0.6
Staphylinidae larvae	0.6	6.0
Curculionidae	3.7	1.4
Elateridae	2.2	22.0
Other *Coleoptera*	1.6	0.6
Tipulidae	6.4	64.0
Other *Diptera*	5.7	0.5
Chrysomelidae	0.1	0.5
Dermaptera	0.6	6.0

(Fig. 6.4). Despite this, it is the arthropods that they eat during the first three weeks of life that are crucial to their survival. Indeed, we found that chicks in broods which suffered less than 50% mortality had eaten a three times greater weight of arthropods than the rest. Those chicks with better survival had also eaten proportionally more plant bugs and sawfly caterpillars.

The amount of arthropod food available to our radiomarked broods largely determined their survival (Fig. 6.5). Consequently broods feeding in areas with few arthropods had larger ranges and suffered heavier mortality than those feeding in areas where food was more abundant.

One potential problem for broods which stay within a small range is that they may be at greater risk from predation (Sonerud 1985). In some cases brood movements might be influenced by predator avoidance. If the predator 'expects' to find its prey

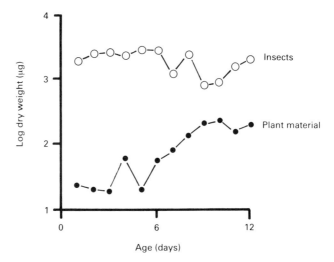

Fig. 6.4 By analysing chick faeces, insects and other arthropods were found to be important early in the chick's life but plant material such as the seeds of *Poa annua* and *Agrostis* sp. become more important in the diet as the chick grows.

species feeding in a certain patch of habitat, or has had previous hunting success there, it is likely to return to the area in an 'area concentrated search'. Geir Sonerud argues that area concentrated search is an efficient predator strategy for exploiting prey with a clumped and relatively stationary distribution. Red grouse chicks,

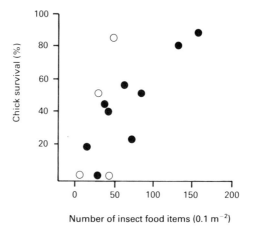

Fig. 6.5 The survival rate of chicks is directly related to the density of insect food available in the chicks' home range. Each point is a radiomarked brood. (Closed circles = Damerham, open circles = Lyons Estate.)

for example, visit 'bog flushes', wet areas on the moor which produce an abundance of insects on which the chicks feed during their early lives (Hudson 1986). Predation at these sites might therefore be an important source of chick mortality. If predators learn that some habitats are better for pheasant chicks they might concentrate their searching activity in them. Also, if a predator finds a brood and takes a chick it will be more likely to relocate them if they only have a small range. If these hypotheses are correct then those broods with the smallest ranges would be expected to suffer the heaviest predation. However, as we have seen, it is the broods with the largest ranges that have the lowest survival, probably as a consequence of food shortages, and it would seem that predation is of secondary importance to insect abundance in determining chick survival. This does not mean that predation of chicks does not occur or that it is of negligible extent. Underhill-Day (in prep) found that, for the marsh harrier, pheasant chicks represented an average 10.2% of the diet during the breeding season.

The habitats selected by broods largely reflected the amounts of arthropod food which they contained. Sixty-eight per cent of 206 radio-locations of eight broods during the first four weeks of life were in cereal fields and only 8% occurred in woodland. Broods significantly preferred feeding in areas of rough grass, weedy strips and weedy areas within fields which contained more food. They avoided woodland and winter wheat which contained less food (Table 6.2). Such selection agrees well with previous studies (Kozicky 1957, Hanson and Labinsky 1964, Warner 1979, Meriggi 1983). In Illinois, hay and oats, with presumably high numbers of arthropods, were selected by broods in preference to corn and soybeans.

Table 6.2 The amount of arthropod food sampled by vacuum net in habitats in which radiotagged broods were located feeding during their first two weeks of life, expressed in dry weight (µg per 0.1 sq m)

Habitat	Arthropod biomass (µg)
Weeds and weedy areas within crops	7740
Winter barley	2490
Spring wheat	5350
Maize	1820
Winter wheat	1280
Woodland ground flora	2730

It should be noted here that the areas of woodland examined in this study were mature plantation or unmanaged high forest. There is some evidence that areas of newly cut coppice or clear-fell can provide good conditions for chick production, but their comparative benefits remain to be quantified.

So, can this dependence on an arthropod diet explain between–year variations in the survival rate of pheasant chicks, and what are the likely consequences to pheasants of current pesticide use?

Pheasant broods have been counted on annual partridge brood surveys by Dick Potts and his co-workers on a 6200 ha area of mixed and arable farmland on the South Downs in West Sussex (described by Potts and Vickerman 1974). These workers also sampled the numbers of cereal arthropods at the beginning of June each year. We can use their data for the period 1970–85 to examine the effects of between–year differences in insect abundance on pheasant chick survival. Seven groups of insects together with average May temperature explained 95% of the annual variation in the survival rate of chicks (Table 6.3). The most important arthropod groups in this respect were ground (carabid) and leaf (chrysomelid) beetles, together with the cater-pillars of sawflies and *Lepidoptera*, which explained 67% of the variation in survival.

In Illinois the survival of pheasant chicks declined from 78% in

Table 6.3 Multiple regression analysis of chick survival, insect abundance and mean May temperature during 1970–83 on the Sussex study area

Insect group	Partial regression coefficients
Carabidae	13.27^{**}
Chrysomelidae	5.74^{**}
Lepidoptera and sawfly larvae	2.79^{*}
Heteroptera	-0.52^{ns}
Jassidae and *Delphacidae*	-0.02^{ns}
Curculionidae	-5.08^{ns}
Aphididae	-0.01^{ns}
Mean May temperature (°C)	-2.32^{ns}
Constant	35.9
Explained variance (%)	95.0
Degrees of freedom	13

$^{*} P<0.1$; $^{**} P<0.01$; ns Not significant

the early 1950s to 54% in the late 1970s, largely as a result of a reduction in the area of hay and oats, preferred habitats of broods because of high arthropod populations. Over this period there have been increases in the use of pesticides on the ever-expanding areas of crops such as corn and soybeans which are replacing the hay and oats. So it is a case of both directly and indirectly taking the food from the chicks by removing their preferred habitat and destroying food insects during the course of farming the new ones.

Without food with a protein content exceeding 14% chicks grow more slowly and die under experimental conditions and in the wild they starve if such food is not available. Mortality of captive chicks has been shown to be directly related to levels of protein in the diet (Scott, Holm and Reynolds 1955, Woodward, Vohra and Snyder 1977, Warner, Darda and Baker 1982). Under poor weather conditions the insects which provide this important protein are not as active. Therefore starvation and chilling go

Plate XI. Small invertebrates such as this heteropteran larva (*Palomina sp.*) are preferred chick food items. (*D.A. Hill*)

Plate XII. Another favoured food item is this heteropteran bug (*Lygocoris sp.*) (*D.A. Hill*)

hand in hand and it is often difficult to separate out the effects of weather and food supplies on survival.

How then has the survival of pheasant chicks been affected by changing agriculture? We know that grey partridge chick survival declined during the 1950s and early 1960s due to the increased use of pesticides and declining insect abundance. However, data for the pheasant are only available from 1970 and there is no evidence of a decline. Pheasant and grey partridge broods both

Table 6.4 Pheasant brood sizes on areas with sprayed and unsprayed cereal headlands on the Hampshire study area in 1984 (Rands 1985)

Area	Average brood size ($\pm$se)	
	Sprayed	Unsprayed
1	3.90 $\pm$ 0.85 (10)	6.90 $\pm$ 1.03 (10)
2	5.00 $\pm$ 0 (1)	8.00 $\pm$ 2.00 (2)
3	2.00 $\pm$ 0.44 (7)	6.82 $\pm$ 0.70 (17)

Analysis of variance: F_1 between treatments 8.14, $P=0.007$; F_2 between areas 1.06 (ns); F_1 interactions 0.58 (ns).

feed on the same foods in the same habitats and their annual rates of survival are correlated, such that we found, for the North Farm study area during 1969–1985, a correlation of $r=0.612$, which was highly significant. It is quite possible that pheasant chick survival declined at the same time as partridge chick survival and that the consequences for populations were hidden by the effects of rearing. However, we have no direct evidence to support this.

Many farmers are presently prepared to spray only certain pesticides, selected for their limited side–effects, on the headlands of their cereal fields in an attempt to bring back some of the wildlife lost over the past three decades, especially of course the chicks of wild gamebirds. Recent research has shown that such practices, while affecting approximately only 6% of the average field size, can make significant differences to grey partridge and pheasant populations in the autumn by increasing the survival rate of chicks (Table 6.4). This happens because weeds, particularly broadleaved species such as knotgrass and corn chamomile, are left to flourish, providing habitats and food for those insects crucial to a chick's survival. Some widespread fungicides have also been demonstrated to kill a number of insect groups (Sotherton *et al.* 1987), and this further compounds the problems faced by chicks. Experiments leaving some headlands unsprayed with the more detrimental compounds have not only benefited gamebird chicks but also butterflies and many of the rarer arable weeds. Tremendous resilience is shown by the seeds of many arable weeds which are able to germinate after many years of dormancy. We return to the effects of selectively sprayed headlands on non-game species in a later chapter.

7   Reared Pheasants in the Wild

'Had only a portion of the money, lost in failures in the hand-rearing of pheasants, been spent in restoring the wood mentioned, it might still have been a good covert; now it is a waste, that can be seen through from side to side − an unbroken expanse of dead bracken, fifty acres in extent, where pheasants are only attracted by constant feeding on bare spots.' John Simpson 1907.

Pheasants have been hand-reared for shooting for generations. In Victorian times, necessarily labour−intensive schemes were set up on many of the large estates in Britain with the aim of producing good quality birds to fly over the guns from November onwards. In this chapter we will concentrate on the fate of these hand-reared birds once they are liberated into the wild. First though, we will outline the current trends in hand-rearing on British estates and describe the different systems by which pheasants are raised.

Using the National Game Census we have investigated trends and fluctuations in the numbers of pheasants hand-reared and shot over the past 25 years. The numbers shot per square kilometre of those areas surveyed has increased from 67 in 1961 to 107 in 1985, and the numbers hand-reared and released for shooting have increased from 53 in 1961 to 180 in 1985 (Fig. 7.1). Consequently total numbers shot, which is a combination of both wild and hand-reared, has not increased at the same rate as total numbers reared. If we plot the ratio of total shot against total reared for each year, we find a dramatic decline suggesting that increased rearing of pheasants has not led to a corresponding increase in

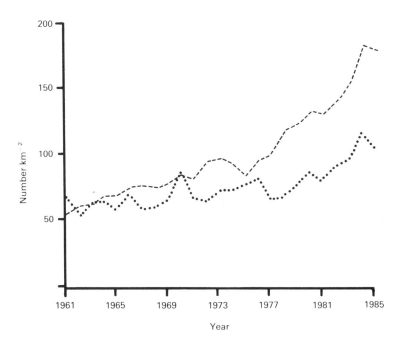

Fig. 7.1 The increase in numbers shot (dotted line) and hand-reared (dashed line) per square kilometre on British shooting estates during 1961–1985.

the wild stocks (Fig. 7.2). This finding poses many interesting questions regarding, for example, the contribution which hand-reared birds make to future breeding populations in the wild, as well as the possible effects of overexploitation of the wild population during the shooting season.

These are questions which we hope to tackle in our chapter on management and exploitation. But in order to understand how this dramatic increase in and reliance on hand-rearing has come about, we need to consider changes in techniques of gamekeeping.

TECHNIQUES FOR REARING PHEASANTS

There are three basic ways of rearing pheasants:

(a) The open field rearing system in which bantam or similar hens, housed in coops, were used as foster-parents to incubate eggs either picked up from the wild, or obtained from penned birds. This is an old, established practice. The bantam foster-parent incubated the eggs within the coop and brooded the chicks as if they were her own. Some food was usually provided but this was often of a very poor quality and a significant amount of the diet of the chicks would be insects which they found for themselves. Since the birds were not enclosed, except at night, a continuous guard against predators was needed to avoid serious losses. Consequently a release pen was not needed and the birds were liberated at a number of sites on the estate. It was thought good practice to release about one broody bantam in every six so that they could range about in the woods with the young poults. After the poults began roosting in trees the broodies were removed.

(b) Movable pens. With improvements in the foods manufactured for young chicks it was no longer necessary for them to be given access to a grass run to forage for themselves. Enclosing the chicks in pens meant that there was less need to control predators although it did lead to problems with disease. The solution to this was to regularly move the pens to fresh ground, hence the name of this system. Poults were then released into the woods in much the same way as with the open-field system.

(c) Intensive rearing systems. The next development was to do

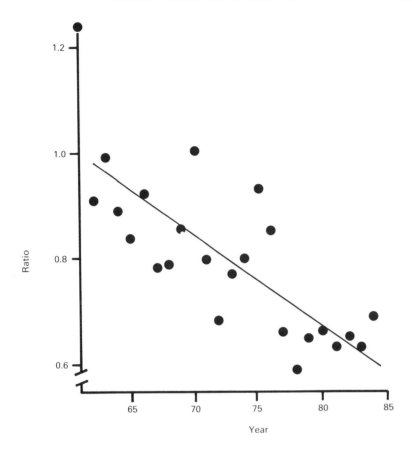

Fig. 7.2 The ratio of total shot divided by total reared has been declining during the period 1961–1985.

away with the bantam foster-parent. Improvements in the design of mechanical incubators to hatch the eggs combined with brooder units to keep the young chicks warm led to great improvements in the efficiency of rearing. While one man could raise 1000 chicks per year using movable pens, the same man could increase this to 5000 using artificial incubation and brooding. When the chicks are two or three weeks old they are let out into runs to harden them to life in the wild. When aged about six weeks they are moved into open-topped release pens in the woods from where they disperse into the wild. Nowadays, many birds are produced in commercial game farms in intensive units and sold to syndicates or game managers, doing away with many of the problems of rearing as far as the individual shoot is concerned.

Once the birds have been reared and moved into the woods the second part of the story begins. To appreciate the factors affecting these hand-reared birds we need to know more about the densities of birds released into different woodlands.

RELEASING STRATEGY AND WOODLANDS

We analysed the National Game Census data for 1982 and plotted the number of pheasants released per unit area of woodland against the proportion of the estate devoted to woodland (Fig. 7.3). The relationship follows a curve (negative exponential) showing that estates with only small amounts of woodland still release large numbers, which consequently means that densities of pheasants at the release site are high. We can infer from this that on many estates there is little regard for woodland area when planning the release programme.

It is not necessarily the large estates which release the largest numbers of birds. Indeed, a plot of total numbers released for

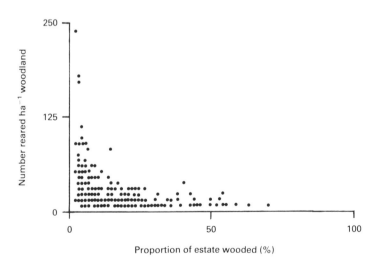

Fig. 7.3 The number of pheasants reared per hectare of woodland is negatively associated with the amount (%) of woodland on the particular estate. This shows data for over 100 estates in the National Game Census for 1982.

each estate in the National Game Census for 1982 shows that there is no relationship with the size of the estate (Fig. 7.4).

To all intents and purposes therefore, pheasant releasing is a 'numbers game' with little regard being paid to those habitat features prevailing on the individual estate. So what actually happens to those individuals which are released, often at a high density? In the next sections we will discuss survival of these released birds together with their subsequent contribution to breeding populations.

RELEASING INTO THE WILD

There are two main and different ways in which pheasants are released into the wild. The first entails the liberation of poults in July or August prior to the beginning of the shooting season in November. This is primarily intended to increase the numbers available for shooting although the contribution made by surviving birds to existing breeding stocks is often quoted as a secondary or subsidiary aim. The second method, rare in Britain, involves releasing adult birds in the spring, which is solely an attempt to increase the size of the breeding population. However,

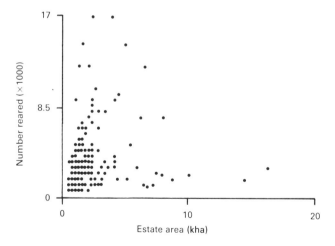

Fig. 7.4 It is not necessarily the largest estates which release the most pheasants. Data from the 1982 National Game Census.

some people release birds of different ages at almost any time of the year.

SURVIVAL AFTER RELEASE

It has generally been found that hand-reared birds undergo their heaviest losses and greatest mortality between release and the start of the shooting season, a period during which they are exposed to the dangers and rigours of life in the wild for the first time. We know from a range of American studies that a larger proportion of hand-reared birds are shot if they are released near the beginning of the shooting season as opposed to a few weeks or even months prior to it. This suggests that the losses are continuous from the date of release although there has been little detailed research regarding the timing and causes of losses.

To discover more about the survival of hand-reared pheasants after release, the survival of 446 hand-reared poults was examined on Lyons Estate in Co. Kildare, Ireland. Pheasants were placed in a pen when six weeks old and within four weeks most were regularly flying in and out each day to feed and roost. In order to follow the survival of individual birds, each was fitted with a numbered wing marker. By reading these tags, clearly visible over the wing feathers (Fig. 7.5), and searching for the tags or remains of dead birds, it was possible to obtain a short life history of each bird. Daily watches were carried out both within and outside the pen.

A method for analysing data of this sort has been developed by Buckland (1981) who used it to examine the survival of marked galahs, a species of parakeet, in Australia (Buckland *et al.* 1983). Using this technique we were able to calculate the survival of the released birds from the pen in some detail (Robertson 1988b).

The survival curve of these hand-reared birds from the date they were placed in the pen is presented in Fig. 7.6. This is plotted on a logarithmic scale so that changes in the slope indicate changes in the death rate; a steep slope reflects high losses and a shallow slope corresponds to a lower rate of loss. During the first thirty days after being placed in the pen the death rate was relatively low as the majority remained in the pen and were safe from predators. However, between thirty and eighty

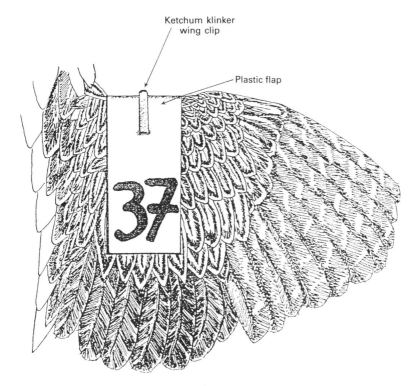

Fig. 7.5 Attachment of a patagial wing tag.

days, as the birds began to venture out of the pen, the rate of loss was very high, 60% of all losses occurring during this period. After eighty days the death rate slowed and remained relatively constant, with a suggestion of a lower rate amongst birds over one year old.

Obviously, the extent of losses will be influenced by a great many factors including predator numbers, the surrounding habitat, weather, the methods by which the birds were reared, their genetic origins and their management during release. The extent of the losses in this example only reflects the local conditions although the timing of changes in death rates should be of wider significance. We might expect to find that most losses of hand-reared birds occur during their vulnerable emergence period from the pen; the number and proportion lost will depend on how well each estate manages its releases. Important factors might include how well the release pen is constructed, how good is the patchiness of the

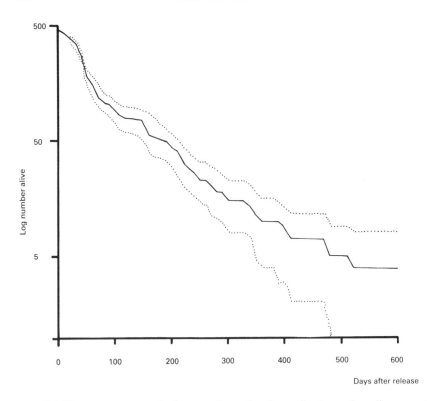

Fig. 7.6 The common survival curve from the date of release for all years at Lyons plotted on a log scale. The area between the dotted lines represents 95% confidence limits.

vegetation within which birds spend their first free days having left the pen, and how good is the control of predators in the immediate vicinity.

Tags and remains of 259 of the original 446 birds were found during searches of the surrounding lands, the probable causes of death being outlined in Table 7.1. Predation was the main cause of loss and, due in part to the relatively low number of predatory species in Ireland, it was usually possible to identify the species involved. The most useful pieces of evidence in this regard were the wing tags: most predators do not seem especially keen on eating pheasant wings, especially when they also carry an indigestible plastic tag. These tags, accompanied by wing feathers, usually bore teeth marks which gave valuable clues as to the predator involved, while the portions of the carcass removed and

Table 7.1 The causes of death of 259 hand-reared pheasants from a total of 446 released over three years

	n	%
Fox predation	166	64
Pen deaths	50	19
Road casualties	12	5
Drownings	11	4
Cat predation	6	2
Badger predation	5	2
Sparrowhawk predation	1	1
Other/unidentified	8	3
Total	259	

the way it had been eaten were also very useful. By comparing corpses found with those where the cause of death was known with some degree of certainty, such as where the predator was seen feeding from the kill or the remains were accompanied by distinctive droppings, we were able to construct a picture of the importance of various predators to hand-reared pheasants. Foxes accounted for 93% of the losses to predation while small numbers were also taken by feral cats, badgers and sparrowhawks. None of these latter species could be considered to cause any significant degree of loss and only took young birds soon after release, hence the fox was the only significant predator in this study (Robertson and Whelan 1987b).

For this reason many British estates run anti-fox fences around release pens, electrified wires which fend off the predator before it attempts to either enter the pen by making a hole in the wire or to take birds 'jugging' (roosting) up against the wire for the night.

Understanding the survival of the poults immediately after re-lease is somewhat confused by the range of dates on which each bird first left the pen. Taking this date as the day on which each bird was first seen outside it was possible to calculate the death rates of the birds from the time each left the pen (Fig. 7.7). What was previously described as a high rate of loss between thirty and eighty days after being placed into the pen can thus be more accurately put as a very high rate of loss of birds during the first twenty days after they first venture out of the pen. This was also associated with a high rate of fox predation as shown by the

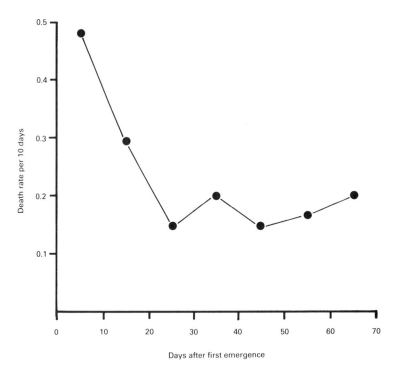

Fig. 7.7 Deaths of released poults at Lyons were found to be highest during the first 20 days after emergence from the release pen.

discovery of carcasses, and a rise in fox activity around the pen. Fox activity was monitored by counting the number of their scats found on set walks within 200 m of the pen and on a control area (Fig. 7.8). The number of scats found around the pen after the birds had been placed in it rose significantly for the following two months.

Foxes were without doubt the main predator of hand-reared birds in the Irish study. This also appears to be true in Britain. Mike Gill (unpublished) examined the causes of death of hand-reared pheasants on an estate in Hampshire where large numbers of birds were released. Although the number of birds lost in total could not be determined it was possible to gain some insight as to the main causes of death. From tags found it appeared that predation accounted for at least 45% of all losses. Of those birds lost to predators, 80% were killed by foxes, reinforcing the

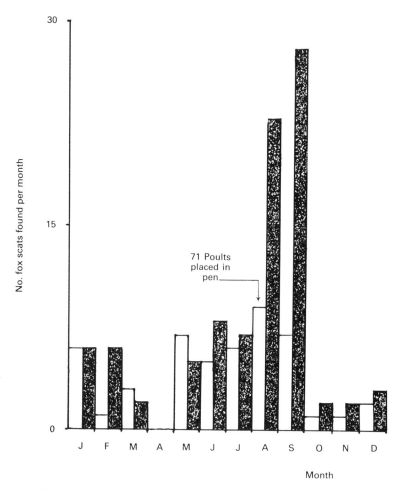

Fig. 7.8 The numbers of fox droppings found around the release pen on Lyons (dark columns) showed a sharp rise following the placement of birds within the pen compared to the number found on a similar area with no release pen (open columns).

position of this species as the most serious danger to hand-reared pheasants.

Although foxes are important predators of pheasants, especially of hand-reared birds, the pheasant is not an especially important prey item for the fox, usually less important than hares, rabbits or small mammals.

Fox diet can be ascertained by collecting droppings and analysing their contents. Some part of almost every creature eaten by foxes is indigestible enough to pass through the gut and still be recognisable. Although the mammals in the diet can be identified to species by the characteristic markings on the hairs that pass out in the droppings, bird feathers can usually only be separated into general groups such as 'gamebirds' or 'songbirds'. There is usually no way of distinguishing between pheasant and partridge remains from feathers found in droppings.

On the Irish study area, pheasants were the only gamebird and this allowed the proportion of pheasant in the fox diet to be determined without encountering this problem (Robertson and Whelan, 1987b). From 210 droppings analysed, only 1.9% contained pheasant remains. There was a noticeable peak during August and September when pheasant remains were found in 7.8% of 51 droppings examined. This rise was significant and coincided with the release of hand-reared birds which, as we have seen, are particularly easy prey.

Other studies encounter difficulties in separating pheasant and partridge remains. However, as pheasants are nowadays far more numerous than partridges in Britain any estimate of the proportion of gamebirds in the fox diet will largely reflect the occurrence of pheasants. Macdonald (1980) found that gamebirds comprised 5.5% of the diet by volume on a syndicate shoot near Oxford. This occurrence rose to 10% during August when hand-reared birds were put down. Reynolds and Tapper (1986) estimated that gamebirds comprised 21.5% by volume of the diet of foxes on estates on the Hampshire-Dorset border. Although gamebirds were less important than either hares or small mammals in their study, the foxes managed to consume the equivalent of 75% of the total spring population of gamebirds on the study area.

Although the fox is the most prominent predator of pheasants in Britain and Ireland, this is in the virtual absence of birds of prey capable of taking adult pheasants. Species such as the goshawk in Europe or red-tailed hawks and great-horned owls in America can be significant predators of pheasants.

Kenward (1977) studied goshawk predation on released pheasants on an estate in central Sweden where 4300 hand-reared birds were put down each year. He estimated that goshawks took around 800 of these birds, almost 19% of the total, and that predation was most intense between release in August and the beginning of the hunting season in mid−November. In a further paper (Kenward 1986) he discusses how releasing large numbers of pheasants can attract higher densities of goshawks to an estate and how these birds then spend more time concentrating on pheasants as a prey item. This is both a numerical and a functional response of a predator to increasing prey density.

Although goshawks can be a significant predator in some countries they are scarce in Britain and have little impact on our pheasant populations. However, some of our birds of prey will occasionally take pheasant chicks or poults, for instance marsh harriers preying on gamebird chicks as described earlier (Underhill-Day, in prep.). However, the pheasants most vulnerable to birds of prey are hand-reared birds concentrated in open-topped release pens. This predation of young released pheasant poults has been examined in some detail by Lloyd (1976). He estimated that predation by birds of prey, mainly tawny owls, sparrowhawks and buzzards, accounts for between 0.7 and 1.7% of all the pheasants released, an insignificant figure compared to the losses from foxes. None of these birds will normally take adult pheasants, although the authors can recount one occasion where a small adult hen pheasant was killed by a female sparrowhawk. Tawny owls will typically only take poults up to 12.5 weeks old, sparrowhawks rarely take a poult over 12 weeks, while buzzards restrict themselves to those aged less than 14 weeks.

David Lloyd also found that the rates of avian predation increased with the number of birds released, a situation similar to that described earlier for fox and goshawk predation of hand-reared pheasants. Another factor affecting the losses from birds of prey was found to be the extent of cover within the release pen. Pens with more than 20% cover in the shrub layer, 1−2 m above ground, were predated less than pens with less shrub cover. Those with at least 60% herb cover, below 1 m, were predated only half as frequently as were those with more open herb layers. Most dramatically of all, he found that bare pens, lacking either shrub or herb layers, were very susceptible to predation and tended to have large losses and mass kills where a predator would kill more birds than it could eat. This is a vital finding, as it demonstrates how habitat considerations can affect the survival of birds and their vulnerability to predation. The current methods, where, all too often, birds are released without regard to the quantity or quality of the available habitat, can only aggravate predator problems.

The killing of birds of prey to protect hand-reared pheasants cannot be justified and is illegal. The losses are usually insignificant and effective deterrents such as flashing lights, tin foil on strings and balloons are available which can deter these predators for the couple of weeks when the pheasants are vulnerable. Common British birds of prey are only able to take pheasants soon after release and concentrate their activities during this period.

The survival of hand-reared birds immediately after release has also been studied in Minnesota by Hessler *et al.* (1970). They fitted five−week−old poults with radiotransmitters and then released them directly into the wild without using any sort of pen. In this case the losses were highest immediately after release, there being no pen to give them any initial protection. When a pen is used the poults are generally about nine weeks old at the time of emergence and will still roost within the pen, gaining access from outside by using funnels placed at regular intervals around it. For a short time this can be an important function of the release pen as fox predation is heaviest at night.

The hand-reared birds in both the Irish study and that of Hessler *et al.* (1970) appeared to suffer a high death rate for two reasons: an increase in fox activity in the area following their release and their greater vulnerability to predation when first exposed to life in the wild. Hessler *et al.* (1970) record losses of 81% in the month following the release of birds directly into the wild and state that predation accounted for 90% of the losses, while a similar study by Burger (1964) records 65% of all losses within the first week.

The disappearance of hand-reared birds is often blamed on their moving away from the point of release. Macnamara and Kozicky (1949) record a released bird being shot 59 km from the point of release, although this is exceptional. Most studies agree that the movements of hand-reared pheasants are usually short, typically over 90% are shot within 3 km of the release site (Paludan 1958, Burger 1964). Robertson (1986) describes the dispersal from the pen after release as the mean maximum distance at which each tagged bird was seen from the pen after emergence

(Fig. 7.9). During this period they dispersed outwards at a rate of approximately 30 m per 10 days. It is fairly clear that the losses through dispersal are usually low compared with losses arising from predation. However, in the absence of evidence many people tend to blame poor results on dispersal. It is well known by gamekeepers but not proven, for example, that manual hand-feeding of poults on woodland rides on a bed of straw causes them to forage for each grain. The need to search for food amongst straw means that less and less time is spent wandering and the birds can be called back to the feed site by the keeper. A bare woodland ground flora might also not only be a reason for birds seeking shelter elsewhere and therefore dispersing, but could be instrumental in making each bird easier for a predator to find. Consequently habitat, food provision, dispersal and predation can be viewed as inextricably linked.

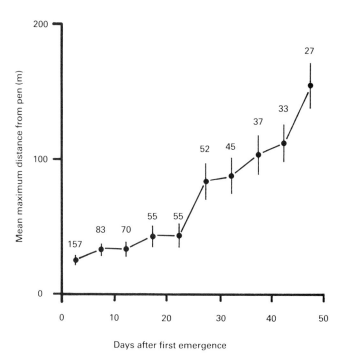

Fig. 7.9 The average maximum distance moved from the pen by poults from each bird's date of first emergence at Lyons. Sample sizes are shown above each standard error bar.

Hand-reared birds can move some distance if released into unsuitable areas or close to some particularly attractive feature. Game-keepers often draw birds towards an area they wish to drive by gradually moving a feeding site from the pen towards the desired spot while some of the more unscrupulous sportsmen draw birds onto their land by planting crops known to be attractive to game on their boundaries to pull in birds released by their neighbours.

The survival of hand-reared birds released in the summer and early autumn can also be calculated from hunting recoveries although this method only allows survival between winters to be established. Paludan (1958) estimated first to second winter survival of hand-reared birds as 15% in Denmark; Bray (1967) presents a figure of 20% for estates in southern England; Robertson (1986) gives survival as 12% in Ireland, while Gindre (1974) quotes 8% for males and 15% for females in France. Thus, as well as the heavy losses incurred soon after release, hand-reared birds also appear to suffer a higher death rate between their first and second winters than wild birds, figures for the annual survival of the latter varying between 20 and 50% (Stokes 1954, Westerskov 1956, Mallette and Harper 1964, Ridley 1983).

OVERWINTER AND PRE-BREEDING ECOLOGY

Those hand-reared birds released during the summer enter their first winter as young adults. These birds begin to mix with the local wild population and by examining their behaviour and role in the social structure of these populations we can see how they have adapted to life in the wild.

One of the most straightforward measures of an animal's condition is its body weight. While this is more crude than the use of a condition index based on correcting body weight for body size, the general idea is that heavier birds have larger reserves of fat, more resources to devote to breeding, and are generally more likely to survive. Fatter birds are usually the fittest − not at all what doctors recommend for us poor humans. We have compared the weights of wild and hand-reared birds in both Britain and Ireland during the winter and found no significant differences, although the Irish birds tend to be rather smaller and lighter (Table 7.2) (Robertson *et al.* 1985). The lack of any significant differences in the body weights of the two groups in the absence of supplementary feeding suggests that the released birds had no difficulties finding natural foods at this time, which has been supported by studies of their diet (Hessler *et al.* 1970, Brennan 1981). Although unfamiliarity with natural foods does not appear to be a problem with newly released birds they may encounter difficulties in digesting a natural diet. Thomas (1986) describes how captive poults raised on a highly nutritious, low fibre pelleted diet do not develop the necessary gut musculature to survive on the bulky diet obtained from the wild once they have been released.

Habitat selection is another important factor deserving comparison between wild and hand-reared birds. Robertson (1985b) compared the numbers of hens of each type caught per day in traps in a variety of different habitats as described in Chapter 3 (Fig. 7.10). There were no significant differences between the two groups, in fact they were so similar as to be virtually identical. Abnormal habitat selection has been recorded amongst hand-reared birds of a number of other species, including chipping

Table 7.2 Winter body weights of wild and hand-reared pheasants from Damerham (Hill 1984) and Lyons Estate (Robertson 1986)

	Reared			Wild		
	mean (kg)	se	n	mean (kg)	se	n
Females (Damerham) February–March	1.10	0.01	47	1.10	0.03	23
Males (Damerham) February–March	1.46	0.03	17	1.52	0.03	10
Juvenile females (Lyons Estate) January–February	0.94	0.03	36	1.00	0.02	41
Juvenile males (Lyons Estate) November–December	1.27	0.03	8	1.27	0.01	77
Adult males (Lyons Estate) October–April	1.38	0.04	7	1.48	0.02	12

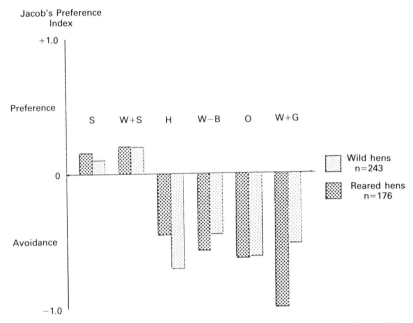

Fig. 7.10 A comparison of the habitat preferences of wild and handreared hen pheasants from winter trapping at Lyons: scrub (S), woodland with shrubs (W+S), hedges (H), bare woodland (W−B), open fields (O), woodland with grass (W+G).

sparrows (Klopfer 1963) and red grouse (Lance 1973), but it appears that those hand-reared pheasants studied had adapted well to wild conditions by the winter.

Male and female pheasants tend to form separate over-wintering flocks; the males, being more aggressive and intolerant, live in smaller, temporary groups compared to the more sociable females, as we have shown in Chapter 3. Examination of the flocking behaviour of hand-reared and wild pheasants can provide information on the degree to which released birds have adapted to anti-predator vigilance and intrasexual aggression, the factors believed to influence flock sizes in the pheasant (Hill and Ridley 1987). Birds in large flocks tend to have a greater chance of being warned of approaching danger as there are many pairs of eyes to keep watch, while competition for rank is usually more intense in larger flocks.

Observations were made of flocks containing mainly wild or hand-reared birds (Table 7.3) but no significant differences were

Table 7.3 The winter flocking characteristics of wild and hand-reared pheasants during January and February on Lyons Estate, Co. Kildare

	Wild			Hand-reared		
	mean	n	se	mean	n	se
Mean flock size	1.68	63	0.13	1.86	88	0.13
Mean size of all male flocks	1.04	21	0.05	1.10	39	0.05
Mean size of all female flocks	1.92	36	0.20	2.33	42	0.19
Mean size of mixed sex flocks	2.67	6	0.36	3.28	7	0.65

found between the two (Robertson 1986). We also calculated an index to look at the number of different birds with which each female associated each time she was seen, as a measure of sociability (Hill and Robertson 1986). This showed that wild and hand-reared females mixed with virtually identical numbers of other birds at any given time (0.783 and 0.784 respectively, n = 38).

In terms of physiological condition, habitat selection and social organisation there were no obvious differences between wild and hand-reared pheasants during the winter. However, these similarities do not necessarily hold during the immediate post-release period when most losses are known to occur. Nevertheless, other significant differences between the two groups are apparent during the winter.

When catching up pheasants for tagging during the winter we have found that hand-reared females tend to be caught in a smaller range of traps and more often in the same trap than their wild counterparts. This suggests that hand-reared females tend to move around less and remain in the same area. This has been confirmed by measuring the sizes of their home ranges (the areas within which they move on a daily basis) by fitting birds with small radiotransmitters in the spring (Table 7.4). On average the

Table 7.4 The home range areas of wild and hand-reared hen pheasants recorded by minimum polygon areas, March and April 1985, as measured by radiotelemetry on Lyons Estate, Co. Kildare

	Wild	Hand-reared
n	17	8
mean	28.36 ha	8.53 ha
se	5.34	2.27

home ranges of the wild hens were over three times as large as those belonging to the hand-reared birds. Despite the dramatic differences in the movements and home ranges of the two groups of females we could not find any similar differences between wild and hand-reared males (Hill and Robertson 1986).

In late winter and early spring the sexual segregation of the flocks begins to break down and the birds move to their breeding ranges. We know that there is an annual movement away from permanent cover such as woods and scrubland into the more seasonal habitats provided by sown fields as they grow and are able to conceal the birds. Both groups of birds demonstrated this same movement away from woodlands in the spring although there was a tendency for the wild males and females to move over twice as far as their hand-reared counterparts, without, however, there being any differences in their habitat selection (Robertson 1986).

Hand-reared pheasants appear to adapt successfully to many of the habits of wild birds by their first winter of life. There are no apparent differences in their habitat use, physiological condition or social behaviour. There was, however, a tendency for the hand-reared birds to be less mobile, both in terms of the sizes of their home ranges and the distances moved between overwintering and breeding ranges. Although these differences may not be apparent to casual observers or appear to be vital at first sight, they indicate significant deviations from the norm and may reflect deficiencies in their behaviours. Such abnormalities may well be important factors leading to the poor breeding success of hand-reared birds in the wild, a situation described in the following section.

THE BREEDING SUCCESS OF HAND-REARED BIRDS

The contribution of hand-reared birds to natural breeding populations has long been a topic of debate. To release such birds into an area where natural stocks are low is a common response to any scarcity and typifies the fundamental lack of understanding by many game-managers of the ecology of the species and its habitat requirements. Sportsmen also regularly liberate adult hens after the shooting season to complement natural breeding stocks and this is particularly common in America. If these released birds do not breed as well as birds bred in the wild then the productivity of breeding populations may be decreased by their presence. Other interesting but as yet unstudied side-effects of releasing hand-reared birds include the role that they play in altering predation levels during the spring. For example, if breeding populations are artificially increased by hand-reared birds which have survived the winter, there could be a density-dependent response by predators to this increase in prey density. Whether wild-reared breeding pheasants suffer as a consequence remains an interesting question. A better understanding of the breeding success of hand-reared birds and their ability to supplement wild stocks will benefit the management of game populations. Beyond its implications for gamebirds it will also give valuable information affecting the conservation of endangered species such as the cheer pheasant where hand-reared birds are being used to reintroduce locally extinct populations in Pakistan (Mirza 1979, Severinghaus *et al*. 1979, Ridley 1986).

During the spring, male pheasants compete to establish breeding territories along the edges of permanent cover and open areas to which are attracted a harem of females as we have shown in Chapter 4. Not all males are successful in gaining a territory and a proportion may remain non-territorial. This does not necessarily mean that they do not breed, as they regularly harass unattended females when given the chance although successful breeding with this behaviour has not been documented and is very difficult to observe. These non-territorial individuals are generally birds in their first spring and are usually lighter than their older territorial counterparts (Ridley 1983).

Data collected in Ireland (Robertson 1986) demonstrated that hand-reared males had lower rates of territory establishment and smaller harem sizes than wild males (Table 7.5). Although all of the wild males successfully gained breeding territories their hand-reared counterparts were not so successful. Almost half of these artificially-reared males failed to establish territories. This comparison must be qualified to a certain extent as the wild male population was not aged in this study. Even so we can say that the observed difference was not simply an age effect as no wild males, irrespective of age, remained non-territorial.

In the same study, amongst those males that did establish territories the wild birds attracted an average of three times as many females to their harems. This comparison is made difficult by the

Table 7.5 The breeding success of wild and hand-reared male pheasants on Lyons Estate, Co. Kildare

	Wild		Hand-reared
No. alive on 1 Feb	29		14
Proportion alive 1 May	0.96		0.86
Proportion breeding	0.96	**	0.57
Mean no. hens per harem	4.86	**	1.62
± se	(±0.53)		(±0.40)

** $P < 0.001$

unknown age structure of the wild population. However, hand-reared males in their second year of life still did not attract as many females as wild males and so the lower success of the hand-reared males does reflect a real difference between the two groups. This combination of fewer territories and smaller harems can be more easily presented by describing the relative breeding success of the two categories. If a female pheasant were given the choice of mating with a wild or hand-reared male, over 80% would choose the wild male.

Despite the smaller number of females attracted by territorial hand-reared males the only detectable difference between their territories and those of wild males was that they tended to be somewhat clumped, most likely related to their limited dispersion from the pen. The proportions and types of different habitats within the territories of the two types of males did not appear to differ. As such the differences in breeding success would appear to be due to the fact that hand-reared males were less attractive to females, rather than that their territories differed dramatically in terms of quality, which we have shown in Chapter 4 is not an important factor determining the female's choice of a male.

As yet we have no clear explanation for the differences between hand-reared and wild birds. However Anderson (1964) reports that wild males tend to dominate hand-reared ones when placed together in a pen at similar ages, while Frömberg and Helgee (1985) describe a relationship between social rank and breeding success in male pheasants, the dominant birds having a greater breeding output. Both of these studies used penned birds and we must wait to see if their findings apply in the wild.

Regarding the release of hand-reared males in the spring,

Robertson (1958) reports that they are subjected to continual harassment from wild birds, usually fail to breed and contribute little towards the population's breeding production. However this may be partly due to their having been marked by cutting off their tails, something that is suspected to lower their breeding success in any case (Geis and Elbert 1956).

Even if hand-reared males did breed on an equal standing to wild-reared birds it would be unlikely to increase the productivity of most populations. As pheasants are polygynous, territorial males typically breed with more than one female so that only a small number of cocks are needed to ensure that all the hens in an area are fertilised. Dale (1951) reports that a breeding sex ratio of at least ten to one does not result in any decrease in fertility in the wild, while penned birds have raised this to fifty to one without detriment. Clearly the addition of hand-reared males of dubious virility will only increase chick production if insufficient wild males are available, a situation that will only occur if they have been subjected to some extraordinarily heavy loss, far greater than anything yet recorded. Our own conclusions are that the release of males in spring is a waste of time and money, which would, as we shall argue later, be better spent on the improvement of habitat for wintering and breeding females.

Although hand-reared males do not seem to make any substantial contributions to natural productivity it would seem that released females ought to stand a much better chance. After all, it is they who produce the eggs and raise the chicks, the ultimate measure of success. To examine the breeding success of artificially raised females that survive the winter, both wild and hand-reared hens were fitted with radiotransmitters and followed through the spring and summer (Table 7.6) (Hill and Robertson in press).

Our results showed that there were no significant differences in the average number of nesting attempts per bird between the two groups, both producing a small proportion of second nests after initial failures. Furthermore, there was no difference in the percentage of these nests successfully hatching. Thus hand-reared females appear to be just as capable of laying, incubating and hatching a clutch of eggs as their wild counterparts. Differences do however arise when we consider the proportions of adult females killed by foxes during the breeding season. The hand-reared birds are almost three times as vulnerable to fox predation

Table 7.6 The comparative breeding success of wild and hand-reared hen pheasants on Lyons Estate, Co. Kildare, and near Damerham, Hampshire, UK (Hill and Robertson in press)

	Wild		Hand-reared
No. radiotagged hens alive, 1 April	34		15
Nesting attempts per hen	1.16		1.08
% Hens killed by foxes April–August	27	**	80
% Incubated nests hatching	44		45
% Hatched broods containing at least one chick at fledging	81	**	22

** $P<0.001$

both before and after incubation. When actually sitting on the nest both wild and hand-reared hens are especially vulnerable to predation; it is only when off the nest that differences are apparent. As a result of the loss of adult hand-reared females when with a brood, the chance of a wild hen rearing a brood to fledging is nearly four times that of their released counterparts. Using these figures it is possible to estimate the numbers of broods fledged by 100 wild or hand-reared females alive at the beginning of April. The high rate of predation on adult females results in the hand-reared birds only fledging a quarter of the number of broods fledged by wild ones.

These results can further be used to illustrate the effect of having an increasing proportion of hand-reared females in a breeding population of given size. As the proportion of hand-reared females increases, fewer chicks are produced by the population as a whole (Fig. 7.11). These results are derived from studies on estates without full-time gamekeepers. It is possible that the removal of predators by a keeper would increase the production of chicks by hand-reared birds but as such management also increases the breeding success of wild birds (Potts 1986), it still may not bring hand-reared birds up to par with the wild population.

Many American states have, at some time, released adult female hand-reared pheasants in attempts to supplement the natural breeding stocks and increase the production of young. Jarvis and Engbring (1976) in Oregon describe how such a release resulted in 335 females producing 17 chicks, a total of just 0.05 poults fledged per female. Ellis and Anderson (1963) report 0.05 young

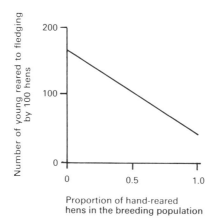

Fig. 7.11 The decline in the number of young pheasants reared to fledging age per 100 hens in relation to the proportion of hand-reared females in the breeding population. (Assumes a mean brood size at fledging of four chicks.)

per hen in a similar situation in Illinois, while another study had the most success with one young poult fledged per female released. These poor results are typically associated with high rates of mortality amongst the newly released birds. Clearly none of these rates of production is high enough to make any substantial increases in the breeding populations of successive years.

Haensly *et al.* (1985) examined the survival and productivity of spring-released females in Oregon using radiotelemetry. By careful planning of the release dates to coincide with the rapid growth of vegetation in the spring they increased female survival and raised productivity from 0.03 to 0.4 young per female released. Despite this increase in the production of young by over ten times they concluded that spring releases were still not an economic method of increasing autumn populations from the chicks so produced. They estimate that the cost needed to produce one extra poult through spring releases of adult females could be used to artificially rear and release seventeen other young birds for release in the autumn.

In Sweden, Brittas, Marcström and Kenward (pers. comm.) found similar results to Haensly *et al.* (1985). Spring-released hens suffered high losses and this seriously decreased their production of young. In three of the four years in which they followed the breeding success of wild and spring-released hens the differences in chick production could be accounted for by heavier losses of adult released hens. However, in 1985, a year when chick survival was generally high, they found that amongst those wild or reared hens that successfully raised broods, those from wild parents contained more chicks. This cannot be attributed to differences in adult survival and it would appear that the hand-reared hens were losing their chicks to some other cause, possibly predation. Although numerous studies recount the poor survival of hand-reared birds, theirs is the first to suggest that they encountered difficulties in successfully raising a brood once they had hatched a clutch.

These examples are all of cases where hand-reared birds have been introduced into areas that already contain a wild population. If hand-reared birds are to succeed in these circumstances they must not only survive natural dangers but also successfully compete with the resident wild birds.

Hand-reared birds have been used with outstanding success to establish populations beyond the natural range of the pheasant, which extends from the Caucasus, along the Black Sea and east across Asia to China, Korea and Japan. This range has been greatly extended due to introductions by man. Long (1981) records introductions into almost fifty countries and the pheasant is now naturalised throughout the temperate regions of Europe and North America. As the initial introductions were typically small numbers of hand-reared birds the huge pheasant populations of the western world can be said to be the descendants of artificially raised stock. Clearly the release of hand-reared birds does play a role in establishing new pheasant populations.

That hand-reared birds can successfully form the nucleus of a new population is beyond doubt. This does not mean that the same job could not be carried out more effectively by transplanted wild birds. For instance Myers (1970) records how 3000 hand-reared birds were released in an area of Pennsylvania between 1949 and 1964 which was otherwise virtually devoid of pheasants. Few of these birds survived the winters and they failed to establish a productive breeding population. The failure of the hand-reared birds led to a trial introduction of 1000 wild pheasants which had been captured in the grounds of the state prisons! These jailbirds were released onto the area between 1964 and 1966 and rapidly established a breeding population which quickly began to increase in size from less than 100 in the spring of 1965 to almost 500 in 1969. The wild birds succeeded in forming a new population in an area where hand-reared birds had repeatedly failed.

NATURE OR NURTURE?

The disadvantages encountered by hand-reared birds can be summarised in four main points:

(a) They tend to suffer heavy losses immediately after being released. These can reach a magnitude of 65% within one week and 80% during the first month (Burger 1964, Hessler *et al.* 1970).
(b) Hand-reared birds consistently demonstrate a higher death rate than their wild counterparts. Most studies record these losses as being due to a greater vulnerability to predation, especially that caused by foxes (Hessler *et al.* 1970 Robertson 1986).
(c) Hand-reared females tend to have smaller home ranges and both sexes move shorter distances during spring dispersion (Hill and Robertson 1986).
(d) As a consequence of these points, few hand-reared birds survive to breed. Amongst those that do, the males achieve fewer matings and fewer females survive the breeding season to raise chicks than their wild counterparts (Hill and Robertson 1986, in press).

These differences may be due to a wide variety of causes which can initially be divided into those arising from the ancestry or upbringing of the hand-reared birds, the old quandary of nature or nurture.

Hand-reared pheasants are often raised on commercial game farms which produce large numbers of chicks from caged laying stock. In some cases the small stocks used for egg production and lack of selective pressure may result in inbreeding. Furthermore some game farms actively select birds lacking aggressiveness to make them easier to handle. Both of these tendencies could lead to inbreeding depression, genetic defects and lack of competitive ability in the offspring (Woodard *et al.* 1983). In Poland, Pielowski (1981) reports that poults raised from eggs produced by game farm birds suffered double the losses after release of poults raised from the eggs of wild birds. In the same area Majewska *et al.* (1979) compared the physiology of wild and game farm birds and found differences in the structure of the gut, biochemistry of the tissues and also in their behaviour.

The influence of parentage can have an important effect on some hand-reared birds but it is far from the only factor involved. Furthermore many game farms are conscientious in catching up a new set of wild birds each year to form the basis of their breeding stocks which should avoid many of the detrimental effects associated with inbreeding. This is exemplified by the policies of Hungarian and Italian hunting organisations in keeping certain areas as 'wild pheasant refuges' from which they catch up birds for breeding purposes.

Delacour (1977) records thirty-two different sub-species of the pheasant and, at one time or another, most of these have been hand-reared for release in some part of the world. These sub-species are all probably adapted to local conditions and when introduced into a new area some may be more successful than others. Wollard *et al.* (1977) claim that Korean pheasants (*P.c. karpowi*) had greater success than the Chinese sub-species (*P.c. torquatus*) when introduced into Missouri, although these results are open to other interpretations. Similarly, Westerskov (1962) states that black-necked birds (*P.c. colchicus*) survive better in New Zealand than ring-necks. However, most populations are now hybrids of a number of sub-species resulting from successive introductions. For instance O'Rourke (1970) states that although individuals recognisable as either *P.c. colchicus* or *P.c. torquatus* could be seen in Ireland in the 19th century, they can no longer be distinguished. Haensly *et al.* (1985) compared the survival of different strains of naturalised American pheasants when released together but found no significant differences. The sub-species used in any release may be important when introducing a population to a new area but this is generally not an important consideration for most game managers.

Although the genetic quality of hand-reared birds may be reduced in some circumstances, it does not seem a likely cause of the dramatic differences we have found between the wild and hand-reared birds. We must move on to consider differences caused by the ways in which they are reared.

The first difference in the growth of hand-reared chicks compared with their wild counterparts arises from their being raised away from their parents in brooders. Much of bird behaviour necessary for later life is obtained through imprinting. During early life the chicks go through a series of sensitive periods during which their responses to different situations are determined. If the stimulus necessary for the correct imprinting is absent then abnormal behaviour may develop. This was demonstrated by Lorenz (1952) who, in a classic experiment, convinced young goslings that he was their parent, simply by being nearby when they were undergoing the sensitive period for recognising parents. When eggs are hatched in an incubator they are removed from prehatching communication with the incubating female. Heinz (1973) describes how the hen calls to her chicks while they are still inside the egg. If eggs are played these calls while being artificially incubated the resulting chicks associate them with comfort. Playing alarm calls to the eggs makes the chicks run towards the source rather than freezing and hiding as they would under normal circumstances (Bailey and Ralph 1975). The incubating calls of the female also make the chicks more receptive to feeding, caution and other calls encountered after hatching. The absence of such calls and also of the presence of the hen after hatching may produce chicks seriously deficient in imprinted behaviours necessary for life in the wild. For instance, artificially raised birds of other species are known to display abnormal mate choice (Worsely 1974, Cheng *et al*. 1978, 1979), habitat selection (Klopfer 1963, Lance 1973) and unusual responses to new stimuli (Salzen 1963, Rubel 1970).

One study particulary relevant to this topic is the study of gamebird chick responses to predators carried out by Thaler (1986). In this the behaviours of naturally and hand-reared hazel hen, rock ptarmigan and rock partridge chicks were compared when presented with dummy predators. The naturally reared chicks were tested in the presence of their mother who gave alarm calls at the approach of the dummy predators and the chicks responded by freezing and crouching. Hand-reared chicks initially responded in a similar manner but when about three weeks old their responses became weaker, even when the appearance of the predator was accompanied by recordings of alarm calls, until they no longer crouched or even bothered to stop feeding. Clearly, although the chicks hatch with innate responses to potential danger, these must be reinforced by the behaviour of the hen if the chicks are to develop an effective anti-predator response. The hand-reared chicks did not develop this and would presumably be more vulnerable to predators as a result. This conclusion is supported by work in progress by Brittas, Marcström and Kenward. They compared the survival of pheasants reared in mechanical incubators and brooders or under bantams when released in the spring and found that those birds reared with a foster-parent had the lowest rate of loss. Furthermore of those hens still alive three months after release, well into the breeding season, half of the fostered birds had a brood compared with only one in seven of the mechanically reared birds. The fostered hens therefore not only survived best, they also reared more young. As most losses were due to predation it would appear that the absence of the parent or even a foster-parent during the chick's development had a significant effect on their subsequent survival and behaviour.

A further factor affecting the development of hand-reared chicks may be the high density of birds during rearing, often as many as a few thousand chicks being raised in the same enclosure. High population densities have been shown to be related to

Plate XIII. Prior to the development of artificial incubators and brooders, poults were kept with a bantam foster parent in movable pens. (*Hugo Straker*)

Plate XIV. Nowadays, intensive rearing systems enable one man to look after large numbers of poults. (*John Marchington*)

increased stress, lower reproductive performance and to disrupt normal pecking orders in other species (Christian 1956, Rushen 1982). Furthermore, increasing the density of birds also raises the chances of disease transmission. Hudson (1986) has demonstrated the effect of nematode parasite loads on red grouse. Birds with heavy infections produce fewer eggs, raise fewer chicks and are more vulnerable to predation. Also, Kenward (1978) has shown that goshawks selectively kill diseased or defective woodpigeons, while Göransson (1975) suggests that predation by this species may be unusually severe where pheasants are diseased.

Another factor which requires discussion is the high rate of loss immediately after release. Although the factors described above have an obvious role to play in increasing the vulnerability of hand-reared birds, the method of release can also be important. We have demonstrated that the release of poults from a pen can cause an increase in predator activity in the immediate vicinity as the birds begin to emerge. This concentration of inexperienced and vulnerable birds makes for easy and very profitable prey for predators, which are then attracted to the area in greater numbers or spend more time there as individuals — what could be termed a 'bird table' effect.

Once hand-reared birds have moved away from the pen they still typically suffer a higher rate of mortality than comparable wild birds. This may be partly due to their smaller home ranges and relatively sedentary nature. Pheasants live in groups and the strategy used by many predators to increase their success when hunting well camouflaged prey that live in groups is area concentrated search. This involves the predator returning to an area where it has met with previous success in the hope that it will find more of the same prey hidden nearby. If the predators are using this strategy, as foxes are known to do in certain circumstances (Macdonald 1980), then the prey should respond by moving over larger areas to avoid being nearby when the predator returns. It is conceivable that hand-reared pheasants may be especially vulnerable to this sort of predation as they tend to remain in relatively small areas over quite long periods of time.

Our work on hand-reared pheasants in the wild has shown then that most mortality occurs during the period of their emergence from the pen, and that predator activity around the pen increases once birds are placed within it. There are a number of important considerations that arise from this. Firstly, habitat quality would appear to be an important determinant of the success of any release programme. Not only should the pen contain an abundance of shrubby cover interspersed with open spaces for feeding, drying out and so on, but the surrounding habitat should be equally heterogeneous. Shrubby cover may not only reduce predation by making the prey less easy to find, as demonstrated by Lloyd (1976), but should also reduce wandering and improve the holding capacity of the habitat through to the shooting season.

Strangely, habitat at the release site often receives far less attention than it deserves, and this oversight may be costly. We demonstrated in our opening to this chapter that, on some shoots, little attention is paid to woodland area when pheasants are being released. It is as if a number is thought of that will achieve a certain bag per shooting day, and this is all that is required. It is not. Our real concern is for the money which is wasted which could be spent on habitat improvement, creating the right conditions on farmland in anticipation of the times in the year when birds leave the shelter of the woods. These are all matters which strike at the heart of achieving the integration of game management and conservation in general in Britain today, something to which we devote a great deal more time in the final chapter.

8   Shooting and Its Effect on Populations

THE HISTORY OF SHOOTING

The history of hunting small game goes back a very long way. One of the earliest records is of the aristocracy of Egypt killing wildfowl with a form of bolas in 1400 BC (Longrigg 1977).

As discussed in Chapter 1, the pheasant was probably introduced by the Normans and for the first three centuries of its residence in Britain any hunting must have been carried out with long- and crossbows. The first record of a firearm of any description which could be fired from the hand or shoulder dates from 1338 while in 1394 there is the first record of a gun being used against game when a Richard Moffit fired a gun at a buck in Epping Forest.

The use of guns against game increased and was common by the 1450s. Pheasant shooting became increasingly popular and during the reign of Henry VIII the taking of pheasant eggs was punishable by a year's imprisonment. At this time the weapons had slow ignition systems and most game was shot while stationary. During the reign of William III (1689–1702) the flintlock was introduced which greatly improved the ability of the sportsmen to fire at moving targets.

Although there are records of game being shot on the wing during the 1560s it was not until the advent of the flintlock that this became common practice. By the beginning of the 19th century the typical method of hunting pheasants was for a group of sportsmen to walk through a wood and shoot at birds flushed by dogs, usually springer or cocker spaniels. The guns used at this time were long-barrelled, smooth bore weapons. Single-barrelled guns had predominated until the 1790s when double-barrells were used for the first time.

These guns were still dependent on the flintlock system of ignition, a spark caused by flint hitting steel igniting a charge of black powder which set off the main charge in the breech. This system was slow to reload, unreliable in wet or windy weather, and involved an appreciable delay between pressing the trigger and the charge igniting.

The development, in the first decade of the 1800s, of percussion locks using fulminate of mercury to produce the spark greatly increased the reliability and speed of ignition but the resulting weapons were still slow to reload, the charge and shot having to be pushed down the barrel.

The greatest advance in shotgun manufacture occurred with the advent of the breech loader at the Great Exhibition of 1851. Early models were unreliable but by 1877 the design of the modern shotgun was pretty well complete, allowing reliable ignition and rapid reloading.

These changes in shotgun design were reflected in changes in the methods used to kill game. The old methods of walking up birds which would be flushed by dogs gave way to 'battue' or driven shooting where game are flushed by beaters towards a line of standing guns. The developments in sporting weapons allowed large numbers of game to be killed in quick succession and there became a demand for dense game populations to provide adequate sport. It was at this stage that hand-rearing first became a common practice as a short-term method of increasing densities for driven shooting.

Technological developments in firearms during the mid 19th century were paralleled by the expansion of the railways, giving access to previously remote areas such as the highlands of Scotland. This led to the development of large-scale grouse shooting with many hitherto unproductive moors being managed primarily for their game.

In the lowlands the demand for shooting led to extensive pheasant and partridge management. From being a casual winter pastime, shooting became the entertainment of high society, with shooting parties lasting for a week at a time.

Central to the popularity of large-scale driven shooting during the latter half of the 19th century was the passion of the Prince of Wales (later Edward VII) for the sport. He made it fashionable and society followed his lead. The investments made in providing birds for the guns were phenomenal, one saying going that 'Up gets a guinea, bang goes a penny halfpenny, and down comes half a crown'. On some of the largest days, over 4000 pheasants were killed and at these prices a number of notables ended up bankrupt, even though income tax was only 5d in the pound (Garnier–Ruffer 1977).

Pheasant shooting on this scale declined after the First World War although the techniques developed came into use by more people on a smaller scale. Driven pheasant shooting is now the norm on many farms and estates across the country although, thankfully, the days of 4000-bird bags are now behind us.

THE NATIONAL GAME CENSUS ESTATES

The number of game killed per year can provide a simple index of the status of our game populations. Although it is hard to

Plate XV. The management of habitats for pheasant shooting helps to maintain the diversity of lowland farms. (*John Tarlton*)

relate numbers killed to the actual size of the population, it can be used to estimate changes in numbers between years provided hunting intensity remains relatively constant.

The 600 or so estates which contribute annually to the Game Conservancy's National Game Census have been instrumental in monitoring the status of Britain's game populations. Over recent years the Game Conservancy have also obtained sets of historical data, some going back to the early 1800s. Using this wealth of data we are able to monitor the status of game.

For the purpose of this chapter we have selected 39 estates for which we have long strings of data, complete in the sense that there are records for each year. This data set enables us to document historical changes in the shooting scene. Other estates were omitted on the grounds that the details for hand-reared birds were sometimes incomplete, or that the data strings had appreciable gaps in them. The number of wild birds in the bag was calculated on the basis of a constant proportion of the hand-reared birds (41%) being shot each season. This return rate was derived from the Game Conservancy's wing-tagging scheme in which participating shoot managers wing-tag their reared birds and report the numbers shot. Whilst there are differences in the recovery rates of wing-tagged released birds between different estates, related perhaps to game-keeper effort, accessibility of birds to the guns, and the provision of winter cover, we believe that any biases introduced are likely to be small as we are dealing with average recoveries over a 25-year period.

Consequently, the number of 'wild' birds shot is calculated by multiplying the number reared by 0.41, and subtracting this from the total pheasants recorded in the bag. This definition of 'wild' birds includes survivors from previous releases and their offspring. Division of the wild bird element by both the amount of wood-land and the total area of land provides standardised density values with which we can make between-estate comparisons.

THE DEPENDENCE OF SHOOTING ON HAND-REARED BIRDS

There are two ways of investigating the degree to which shooting relies on birds artificially reared and released into the wild. The first is to investigate the relationship between estates.

How strong is the relationship between the number of pheasants an estate releases and the number it shoots? To examine this we must first know more about between-estate variations in shooting pressure. On average, eight guns take part in a typical drive and there is generally little variation in this number between different estates. Shooting pressure appears to be relatively constant be-tween estates, particularly those we shall be considering in this chapter. However, large estates may hold more shooting days than small ones, purely because on large shoots different areas are driven each time. In contrast small shoots may not wish to put continual pressure on one patch of ground, and restrict their number of shooting days accordingly. Over all, shooting pressure per unit area on each estate examined here can be assumed to be constant.

To take the first example, data for the period 1961–1985 for the 39 estates were analysed by averaging the number of wild birds shot and presenting this in terms of numbers shot per unit of total estate area and per unit area of woodland. The number of birds released per hectare of woodland was also calculated. We should point out at this stage that data in the National Game Census are given to us on the basis that they remain confidential. We shall refer only to the county and the estate number which we have assigned, unless specific permission has been granted. One interesting finding from our analysis was that there was much greater variation in the number of wild birds shot per unit area of woodland than in the number shot per unit of the total area of the estate (Table 8.1). Furthermore, the number released per unit woodland was highly variable. This confirms our view that a large proportion of woodland on an estate is not an important prerequisite for a dense pheasant population. Large woods are not as attractive to pheasants as small woods, (Fig. 8.1), as we showed in an earlier chapter.

The average number of wild birds shot over all 39 estates was 0.82 per ha, with a range of 0.1 to 1.5. The number of wild birds shot per hectare of woodland varied between 0.3 and 66.8, with an average of 11.1. An average of 23.3 reared pheasants were released per hectare of woodland on the estates, although this was highly variable, with a range of 0 to 272 birds.

It is not too surprising to find that those estates which reared most pheasants shot more than those which reared few. The slope of the relationship between numbers reared and numbers shot was also close to 1.0 (0.89) and the number of pheasants released explained 43% of the variance in total pheasant numbers shot (Fig. 8.2a). However, when the data were converted to density values the relationship became less clear; the slope declined (0.47), suggesting that when birds are reared at a high density their contribution to the total bag per unit area is relatively less than when few are released (Fig. 8.2b). This is supported by the higher return rates from large releases, a feature we shall discuss shortly.

The second method of investigating the relationship between the numbers of birds reared and the numbers shot is to look at the trends on individual estates. For this purpose we present information from five estates which illustrate the dependence of individual shoots on hand-rearing, and how this has changed through time.

During the immediate post-war years at North Farm in Sussex no pheasants were released, and relatively few pheasants were shot. At this time shooting concentrated largely on grey partridges.

Table 8.1 Wild pheasants shot per hectare of woodland and total land, percent woodland cover, and numbers of pheasants released per hectare of woodland for 39 estates in the National Game Census. Data are means ($\pm$ SE) for the period 1961–1985 inclusive.

Estate	County	Mean area Shot (ha)	Woodland %	Wild pheasants shot per hectare: Woodland	Total area	Pheasants reared per hectare of woodland
1	Wiltshire	491± 2	5.6±1.2	13.9±1.3	0.8±0.1	32.2±2.9
2		1334±20	19.5±0.3	1.3±0.3	0.3±0.1	4.1±0.9
3		450± 1	1.2±0.1	17.4±3.3	0.3±0.1	77.4±7.4
4		372± 1	1.9±0.1	1.9±0.1	0.9±0.1	30.3±1.3
1	Hampshire	945±53	32.4±2.5	3.2±0.3	1.0±0.1	10.9±0.7
2		2023± 0	8.7±0.4	7.4±0.5	0.7±0.1	9.6±0.6
3		2411± 9	19.7±0.3	4.3±0.4	0.9±0.1	11.0±0.8
4		1028±13	30.6±0.7	3.4±0.8	1.0±0.2	10.5±1.8
5		595±13	33.8±1.0	1.5±0.2	0.5±0.1	4.3±0.7
6		1392±41	26.7±1.0	4.4±0.3	1.2±0.1	11.0±0.7
7		1372±44	28.2±0.6	2.1±0.3	0.6±0.1	5.9±0.9
8		1299±49	6.3±0.2	3.0±0.6	0.2±0.1	7.7±1.5
1	Berkshire	760±62	10.2±0.4	4.8±0.7	0.5±0.1	2.7±0.5
1	West Sussex	1375±25	2.8±0.3	51.5±8.8	1.4±0.2	120.0±23.0
2		600±22	34.1±1.4	0.3±0.1	0.1±0	2.7±0.3
1	Kent	1054±23	19.9±0.3	2.9±0.3	0.6±0.1	13.1±0.5
1	Lincolnshire	2983±45	5.9±0.1	12.2±0.9	0.8±0.1	22.3±2.3

Norfolk	1	2520±18	9.4±0.2	8.7±0.9	0.8±0.1	6.5±1.1
	2	1470±19	8.2±1.0	11.9±1.2	0.9±0.1	24.9±2.0
	3	1395± 7	10.5±0.2	7.2±0.8	0.8±0.1	15.2±1.5
	4	2023± 0	7.1±0.1	8.4±0.6	0.6±0.1	13.1±0.8
	5	1348±27	14.4±0.3	5.2±0.4	0.8±0.1	5.2±0.3
	6	1636±33	6.4±0.1	9.0±0.7	0.6±0.1	0
	7	1751±24	14.2±0.2	6.8±0.6	1.0±0.1	3.6±0.5
	8	1415±18	10.4±0.3	11.2±0.8	1.2±0.1	10.4±1.3
	9	1250±29	14.6±0.4	7.3±0.6	1.1±0.1	6.2±1.0
	10	8013±81	9.0±0.3	8.5±1.0	0.8±0.1	0
Suffolk	1	486± 0	15.6±1.0	6.3±0.7	0.9±0.1	1.4±0.3
	2	553±16	4.3±0.1	19.6±2.0	0.9±0.1	26.4±3.7
	3	4097±211	14.3±0.8	7.3±0.9	1.1±0.1	0
	4	1010±15	5.5±0.5	24.1±3.2	1.1±0.1	20.4±2.3
	5	429± 2	16.4±0.4	6.9±0.8	1.1±0.1	8.6±1.3
	6	6439±119	26.1±1.7	6.2±0.7	1.5±0.1	3.8±0.7
	7	1311± 3	8.1±0.1	13.9±1.4	1.2±0.1	0
Essex	1	1214±62	11.7±0.5	3.9±0.6	0.4±0.1	12.9±1.5
	2	606±20	0.6±0.1	39.6±4.6	0.7±0.1	272.0±77.0
	3	580±18	0.8±0.1	66.8±3.9	1.1±0.1	73.5±10.0
	4	505±27	5.1±0.4	8.9±1.4	0.6±0.1	25.9±4.4
	5	1012± 0	10.0± 0	11.0±1.6	1.0±0.1	0

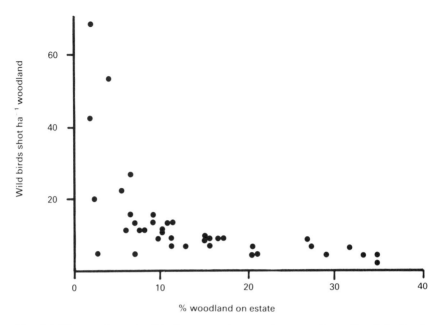

Fig. 8.1 The number of wild pheasants shot per hectare of woodland declined on estates with an increasing amount of woodland cover, suggesting that large woods are not favoured habitats.

During the 1950s pheasants were extensively reared and released and this continued until the late 1960s when the amount of hand-rearing declined. The number of pheasants shot clearly mirrors the number released and a plot of total shot on number released shows a highly significant correlation (Fig. 8.3).

A similar story can be told for Estate 3 in Kent. These data demonstrate the dramatic effect of the two World Wars on pheasant shooting. During the war years few estates released pheasants on their land. Money was too scarce to fuel the indulgence of pheasant shooting, and rearing, keeping and shooting pressure all declined (Fig. 8.4). The subsequent dramatic increase in rearing from zero to about 3500 on the 1000 ha estate was mirrored by an increase in the total number of pheasants shot, the correlation between the two being highly significant with a slope of 0.46.

On Estate 1 in Lincolnshire the war years again saw no pheasants released and many fewer birds were shot (Fig. 8.5). A gradual increase in the numbers reared after the war from 0 to 8000 on the 3000 ha estate has not been entirely mirrored by an increase

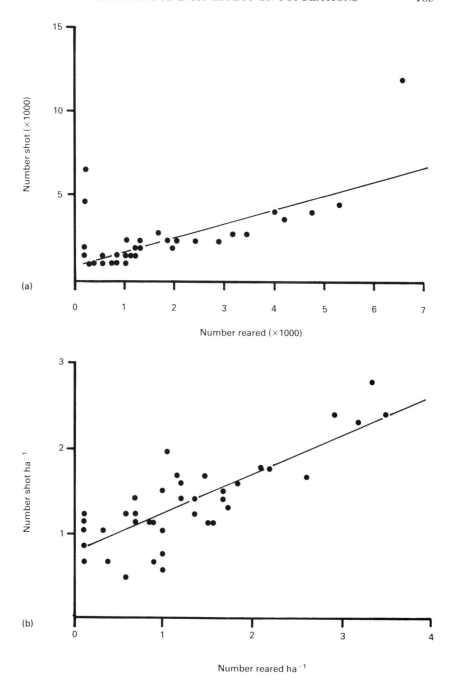

Fig. 8.2 National Game Census data for the 39 estates showing that (a) those releasing more birds shoot more (slope = 0.89), and (b) when converted to per unit area (hectare) the relationship is less clear (slope = 0.47).

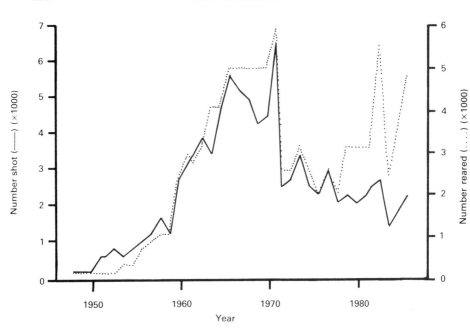

Fig. 8.3 Pheasants shot (solid line) and reared (dotted line) on Estate 1 in Sussex 1947 to 1985.

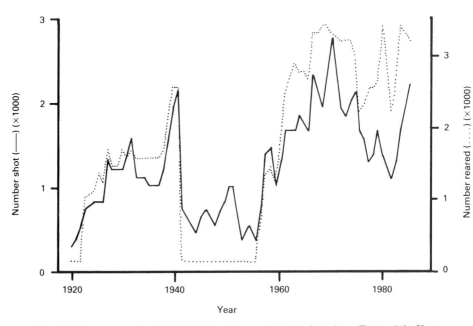

Fig. 8.4 Pheasants shot (solid line) and reared (dotted line) on Estate 3 in Kent, 1919 to 1985.

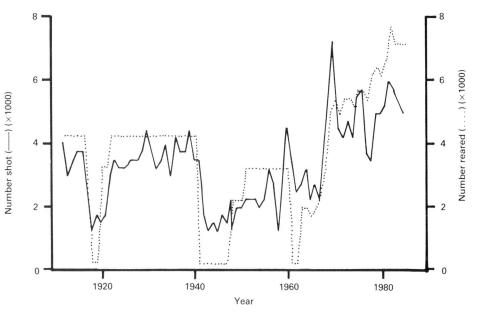

Fig. 8.5 Pheasants shot (solid line) and reared (dotted line) on Estate 1 in Lincolnshire, 1911 to 1985.

in total numbers shot (slope = 0.57), possibly due to some factor affecting wild pheasant production.

On Estate 5 in Suffolk, pheasant bags fluctuated around 400 birds on the 490 ha area in the absence of rearing (Fig. 8.6). An increase in the trend towards hand-rearing from 1965 onwards was mirrored by a rise in the total number of birds shot, the correlation between the two being highly significant, with a slope of 0.56.

The final example we will present is that for Estate 3 in Wiltshire. From 1914 to the early 1960s few pheasants were shot on the 450 ha estate (Fig. 8.7), either on partridge drives or walking up with dogs. By the early 1960s however, hand-rearing was seen as a way to improve the shooting once partridge numbers had declined. The relationship between the numbers of reared birds and total pheasants shot is probably the most dramatic of our five examples in that only in the last 25 years or so have relatively large bags been achieved, and these as a result of hand-rearing. The relationship between the two is highly significant, with a slope of 0.56.

Between estates, there is generally a relationship between the numbers released and the proportion of these shot. Typically

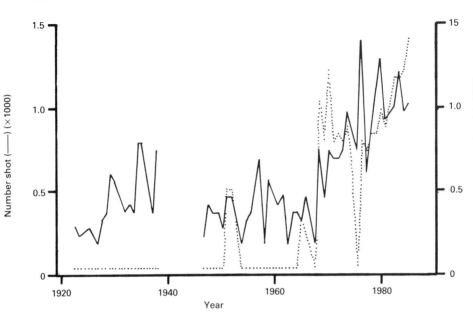

Fig. 8.6 Pheasants shot (solid line) and reared (dotted line) on Estate 5 in Suffolk, 1922 to 1985.

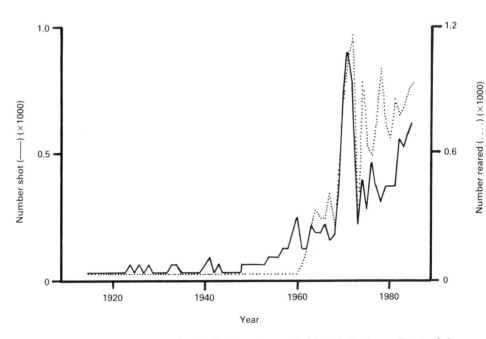

Fig. 8.7 Pheasants shot (solid line) and reared (dotted line) on Estate 3 in Wiltshire, 1914 to 1985.

those estates which release large numbers (expressed as logarithms in Fig. 8.8) shoot a higher proportion of them than those estates which release few. This may be due to the more intensive keepering or shooting on those estates releasing larger numbers of birds.

THE SITUATION ON PURE WILD-PHEASANT ESTATES

Nowadays it is rare to find a purely wild-bird shoot. Those that remain are often either at the point when some small-scale releasing is about to, or has recently taken place, or the estate is surrounded by others who release hand-reared birds. These birds, if they wander, can give a very false impression of the size of the wild population on the neighbouring estates. It is also not unknown for some gamekeepers to release birds in order to ensure

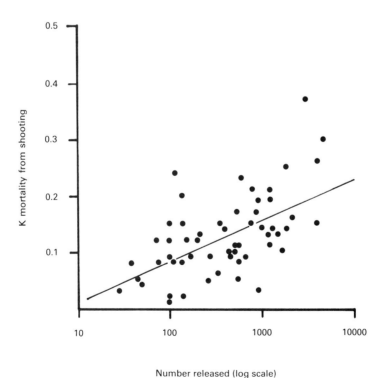

Fig. 8.8 For 55 estates which released wing-tagged pheasants and reported their recovery, the proportion shot (expressed as a log mortality) increased as the number released increased.

some 'wild birds' to shoot. Certainly, many deliberately under-
estimate the number they rear.

We have isolated five estates where as near to wild pheasant
shooting exists as can be found anywhere. The first of these is the
Hardingham Estate in Norfolk. From the late 1800s to 1950 only
wild birds were shot. In the post-war period a small number of
about 400 birds were released per year. However, the calculated
wild bag remained relatively constant but at a lower level than
before the war (Fig. 8.9). In 1970 a programme of spinney planting
was undertaken with the primary aim of improving the habitat for
pheasants. At the same time both the keepering effort and the
rearing programme were increased so that an average of about
600 birds per year were released. During the spinney planting
phase, 40 small coverts totalling about 30 ha were created, increasing the woodland cover on the estate to about 3.5−4%. The
low production of wild birds, whilst still better than on many
estates, is most probably attributable to a change in farming
practice since the war when levels of wild birds were almost

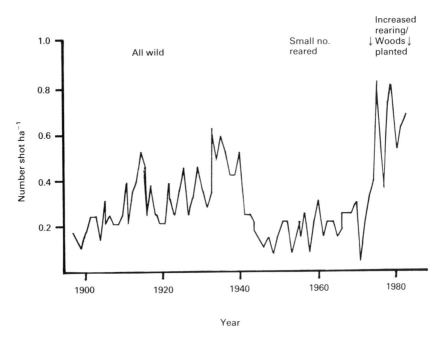

Fig. 8.9 Changes in the number of pheasants shot per hectare on the Hardingham
Estate, Norfolk, 1896 to 1985.

double what they are today. Although the figures appear to show that hand-rearing is good for wild birds in that more are calculated as being shot in or following years when birds are released, the effect is only short term.

The story is different for a 1300 ha estate in Suffolk (Estate 7 in Suffolk) — once a very successful wild bird shoot with, even in the late 1950s and early 1960s, a wild bird bag of nearly 3.5 per hectare over the entire estate (Fig. 8.10). However, there has been a general decline since this time, possibly related to the fact that little after-planting management of the woods and spinneys has been carried out and canopy cover has shaded out much of the holding cover. Perhaps of even more significance is the priority given to farming which now has a very strong position in the estate management and consequently a high reputation to maintain.

Wild bird bags at Estate 6 in Norfolk, a 1600 ha estate where little or no releasing has taken place over the past 25 years, have been relatively low in recent years although there is no firm evidence of a decline (Fig. 8.11).

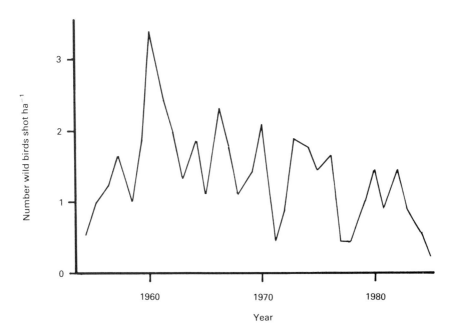

Fig. 8.10 Changes in the number of wild pheasants shot per hectare on Estate 7 in Suffolk, 1954 to 1985.

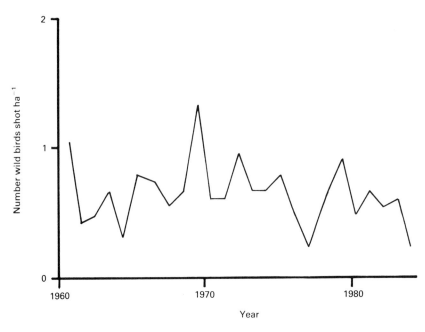

Fig. 8.11 Changes in the number of wild pheasants shot per hectare on Estate 6 in Norfolk, 1961 to 1985.

The 1000 ha Spains Hall Estate in Essex has records going back to 1846; during the 19th century the main quarry species were partridge and hare. However pheasants were reared in increasing numbers over this period until 1934 when the estate reverted to a purely wild bird shoot. There was then a general rise to a peak in the early 60s, and current bags are at a similar level to those in the pre-war period. There is certainly no evidence of a long-term decline. The annual bags since this date are presented in Fig. 8.12.

The 4000 ha Euston estate near Thetford in Norfolk boasts a highly diverse landscape with marginal habitats running alongside streams, shrubby field boundaries and rough field corners, and a diversity of shelterbelts and small woodlands together with the famous park. In all it provides excellent pheasant habitat even though modern farming is probably having a deleterious effect on wild pheasant production. The number of wild birds shot appears to fluctuate dramatically between years (Fig. 8.13) and the present owner has decided to rear a small number on one part of the estate with a view to restocking.

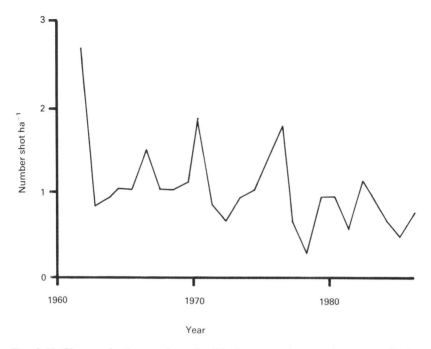

Fig. 8.12 Changes in the number of wild pheasants shot per hectare at Spains Hall, Essex 1961 to 1986.

Historically this estate was made famous by the system of replacing wild partridge eggs with dummies, the originals being placed under bantams out of reach of predatory birds and mammals. The eggs were later replaced just prior to the time of chipping so that their exposure time to natural predators was reduced considerably. The Euston system is seldom practised today although in its time it was a very important development in game management. Increased costs in terms of the labour required will doubtless preclude its use in the future.

These five examples serve to illustrate that whilst we have detected declines in wild birds from shooting records on some estates, the trend is by no means universal. Compounding problems such as the presence of large releases adjacent to some estates are difficult to overcome, as is the fact that estates that still shoot purely wild birds are exceptions in themselves and may not reflect the nationwide status of the wild pheasant. One very sad point is the sheer rarity value placed on wild-bird shoots these days. Active management is the most vital component of any wild-bird shoot and in the next chapter we shall be discussing

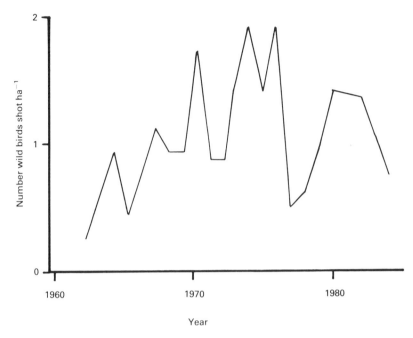

Fig. 8.13 Changes in the number of wild pheasants shot per hectare on Estate 3 in Norfolk, 1963 to 1985.

some techniques to achieve this. For the moment however, we will consider the dynamics of shooting from the point of view of the individual estate.

THE DYNAMICS OF SHOOTING

Whilst comparisons have been made between and within estates over a number of years, the factors operating within estates in each year have received less attention. At the beginning of this chapter we discussed the various methods by which pheasants are harvested in Britain. These methods can have significant effects on the number of birds shot, with relation to both sex and age.

We wanted to examine the rates at which flushed birds are shot to see whether the proportion of birds shot rose or fell as the number flushed increases. In order to investigate this we looked at the data collected on shoot visits in which numbers of each sex flushed and numbers shot were recorded. The first point is that there was the expected tendency for more of both sexes to be shot as the numbers flushed increased (Fig. 8.14). As one would expect the number shot per gun is also higher when more birds are seen on the drive (Fig. 8.15).

In order to test whether the proportion of each sex shot was related to the number of birds passing over the guns on each drive the logarithm of the number of birds escaping the guns (with 1 added to account for zeros) was regressed on the logarithm of the number emerging (again with 1 added to account for zero counts). For males there was no evidence that the proportion shot increased as numbers passing over the guns increased. In other words shooting losses were not related to the number of birds on each drive. However, this did not hold true for females, possibly due to their tendency to flush in groups. However, this is a weak effect and when both sexes are combined it is clear that a relatively constant proportion are shot on each drive.

SEX AND AGE DIFFERENCES IN SHOT POPULATIONS

The birds that are killed during a day's shooting are not always a random selection of the population. Hunters may select certain individuals from within the stock, as occurs on cock-only days. Alternatively, they may unintentionally kill a larger proportion of some group within the population if it is readily found or provides an especially easy target.

One example of this unintentional selection comes from red grouse. Hudson (1985) describes how a greater proportion of old males of this species are shot on driven shoots than would be expected if birds were being shot at random. Grouse pass over the guns either singly or in groups of up to one hundred, and a smaller proportion of those birds in flocks are shot compared with solitary individuals. This is similar to the relationship found for hen pheasants described above, but much more pronounced. In fact, 60% of grouse flying over the guns as singletons are shot compared with only 12% of those in groups of ten. Old male red grouse tend to be solitary during the shooting season as they have left the family coveys and have started to set up their territories. As such they tend to be flushed on their own and are more likely to be shot.

This greater vulnerability of solitary birds to shooting has also been reported by Murton *et al.* (1974) for wood-pigeons and Potts

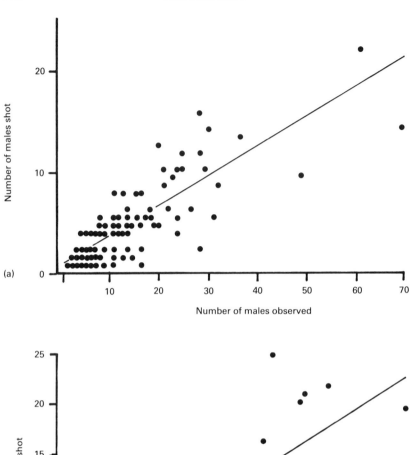

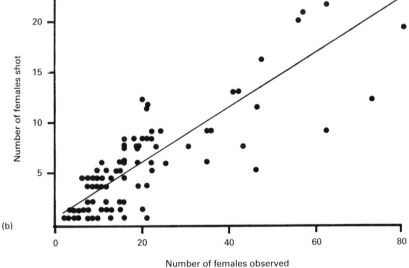

Fig. 8.14 Relationship between the number of each sex observed emerging from cover and shot on 166 pheasant drives. (a) Males, slope = 0.29; (b) Females, slope = 0.27. Some points represent more than one set of data.

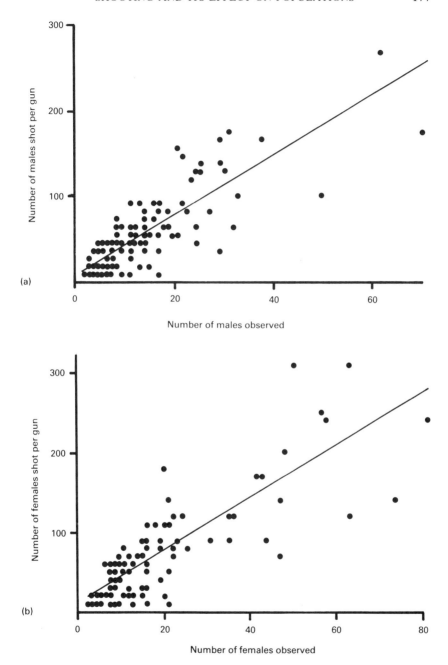

Fig. 8.15 Relationship between the number of each sex observed emerging from cover and shot per gun on 166 pheasant drives. (a) Males, (b) Females. Some points represent more than one set of data.

(1986) for grey partridge. Any feature of the social organisation of a species which leads to one sex or age group being found as singletons during the shooting season could conceivably lead to a heavier shooting mortality amongst that group.

The majority of pheasant studies have been conducted in North America where they are shot by 'walking up' as opposed to on drives. As we have already stated, in the USA much emphasis is placed on selective shooting where, in certain regions and seasons, only cocks are shot and hens, theoretically at least, are left to breed. As a result there is little information on unintentional selection by sex.

Our data from shoot visits showed that there was no change in the sex ratio of the bag in relation to the sex ratio of birds flushed through the shooting season. In other words there was no preference for either cocks or hens shown by hunters as the season progressed. This excludes cock-only days which are normally held at the end of the season's shooting. This absence of a trend in the sex ratio through the season prevailed across all the habitats studied.

Work done in Britain on driven shoots can be compared with studies in the USA where pheasants are shot on rough shoots in which the hunter walks with his dog by his side, taking birds that flush in front of him. The general consensus is that where birds are driven over the guns, there is no bias with respect to age. On the other hand, during rough shoots, first-winter birds are more readily shot than adults. As the season advances the ratio of young birds to old ones has been found to decline steadily. Indeed, in South Dakota a decline in the ratio of young to old birds in the bag from 5.0 to 1.2 has been reported as the season progressed (Kimball 1948). Similar trends have been documented elsewhere in the USA, where birds are shot by walking hunters (Allen 1941, Leopold 1949, Mohler 1951).

However, on rough shoots when hunters patrol at a high density, as on Pelee Island in Ontario, adult cocks appear to have less chance to evade the guns than on lightly shot areas. During the heyday of shooting on Pelee Island hunter density was recorded as one hunter per three acres (1.2 ha) hunted. Under this pressure it is not surprising that the older age categories suffered heavy mortality.

There can be no doubt that driven pheasant shooting produces a whole new set of pressures upon populations compared with those produced by rough shooting. In grey partridges, for example, proportionally fewer birds are shot when they occur at low density, as has been the case in their immediate history owing to the dramatic decline in numbers (Potts 1986). Proportionally more are shot when they are at high density. The reason for this is probably two-fold. First, there is certainly a reluctance to shoot when there are few birds on the ground, a reluctance triggered by the belief that shooting reduces populations and will consequently hamper any attempt to restore their numbers. Second, partridges are more difficult to find when they are at a low density, and consequently too few partridges exist to make a shoot worthwhile.

The consequences of driven shooting to populations have yet to be defined. Driven pheasant shooting on most modern run estates would certainly not be possible were it not for the hand-reared bird. The increased densities resulting from hand-rearing allow increases in shooting pressure. This is felt by both wild and hand-reared birds alike and it is possible that the wild populations of today are being overshot. We must ask the question: What level of shooting pressure can a wild pheasant population sustain?

Let us imagine an estate which releases substantial numbers of pheasants, where the autumn and winter populations are greatly increased and the estate can sustain more shooting than it would have done had it relied purely on wild birds. If released birds survived and bred as well as their wild counterparts this would be relatively unimportant. However, as we have seen in Chapter 7, this is not the case. Furthermore, we have shown above that an average of 30% of the birds driven over the guns are shot on each drive and that both types are as vulnerable to shooting. While most shoots only beat each drive once on any particular shooting day, many will be driven again later in the season. If each drive is shot three times during the year and each time 30% of the birds are shot, this amounts to a 66% kill from shooting. Can wild populations sustain this level of hunting?

MORTALITY RATES DUE TO SHOOTING AND THE THEORY OF HARVESTING

In Britain the proportion of the population killed each year is, to some extent, determined by the estate owner. There is some evidence from the National Game Census and the study on North

Farm that the proportion shot increases as population density goes up. However this levels off at a density of around 200 birds per km^2 (Fig. 8.16). Most of the estates examined in this chapter have pheasant densities above this level and the proportion killed can be viewed as independent of density. In these circumstances the kill is approximately 70% of the autumn population. This is consistent with each bird being driven over the guns three times per season and 30% being shot on each occasion.

Many American states restrict hunting to male pheasants, the females being protected in an attempt to increase the size of the subsequent breeding populations. This may not be the best strategy for ensuring a continued large bag, as described later in this section. The proportion of cocks killed per year has been the subject of many studies and a selection of these are presented in Table 8.2. As male pheasants can fertilise large numbers of females there is little danger of reducing female fertility by over-shooting males. This is also examined in more detail later in this

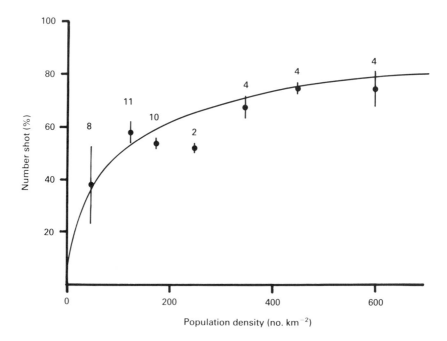

Fig. 8.16 Relationship between pheasant density and the percentage of the autumn population shot per year from the North Farm study area 1953 to 1970, and the National Game Census 1956 to 1976. Mean values ± standard error, with sample sizes shown above each column.

Table 8.2 The percentage of the autumn cock pheasant population shot per year in various states/provinces in North America

% Harvest	Area	Reference
47–76	Michigan	Allen 1947
73–85	California	Harper et al. 1951
86–93	Ontario	Stokes 1954
45–60	Illinois	Robertson 1958
74–76	Ohio	Edwards 1962, 1963
74	California	Mallette and Harper 1964
59–84	Wisconsin	Wagner et al. 1965
76–88	Utah	Stokes 1968
88–93	Pennsylvania	Hartman and Scheffer 1971
60	Nebraska	Baxter and Wolfe 1973
Mean = 74%		

chapter, but even the most extreme hunting pressure of 93% on Pelee Island would not be expected to result in too few males to fertilise the remaining females.

Despite the restrictions on hen shooting in many American states there is still a certain illegal hen kill resulting from error, frustration or an outright disregard for the law. In the light of the illegality of this hunting it is not easy to obtain estimates of its extent. There is, however, one method available. This involves collecting samples of cocks and hens at the end of each season and examining them for shotgun pellets. The assumption in this is that a constant proportion of birds shot at escape alive and therefore the ratio of males to females carrying shot is the same as the ratio killed. As the proportion of males killed is known, it is possible to estimate the illegal hen kill. Calculations of this sort have been carried out by Edwards (1962, 1963) in Ohio, who found that 24–28% of males and 6–7% of the females carried shot. As between 74 and 76% of the males were shot per year this indicates an illegal hen kill of 15–20% of the autumn population. A similar estimate from Wisconsin (Wagner et al. 1965) revealed a 16% illegal hen kill.

There are a number of problems with this method of investigating illegal hen kills. As hens are smaller than cocks they provide a smaller target and it may require fewer shot to kill them. Alternatively, cocks are often considered harder to hit as the deceptively long tail can make hunters aim off target. In the absence of any more details these estimates must stand.

To summarise, an average of 74% (range 45–93%) of the autumn cock population are shot per year in the USA while a further 17% (range 15–20%) of the hens are illegally killed.

The aim of efficient game management should be to obtain the largest bag that can be maintained indefinitely. Obviously if too many pheasants are shot in one year this will reduce the numbers available in subsequent years; alternatively, if too few are shot then these birds will go to waste. Harvest management is all about striking a balance between these two opposites.

To determine how best to harvest any species we first need to understand how the size and productivity of the breeding population is affected by shooting. There are two alternative ways of viewing this problem. The most simple explanation is that every bird shot results in one less bird in the breeding population. This is described as additive hunting mortality. The alternative hypothesis is that shooting only removes a portion of the population that was doomed to die in any case due to some limiting resource. This is known as compensatory mortality. These are both useful concepts to help us understand the effects of hunting, but unfortunately neither is realistic. In most gamebird populations losses through hunting are partially compensated for, a situation somewhere between the two extremes outlined above (Robertson and Rosenberg 1988). This partial compensation allows a population at equilibrium to absorb a certain degree of hunting pressure without detriment.

There are two general mechanisms by which this partial compensation can occur. First, the loss of birds through hunting can increase the survival of other individuals as would be the case if there was only a limited amount of food available during the winter. This partial compensation of overwintering survival includes decreasing the amount of emigration from the area under consideration. The second method of compensation commonly encountered is that decreasing the density of the breeding population may increase the number of young reared by each of the remaining individuals. This has been shown to be the case for the grey partridge where nest success is highest at low densities (Potts 1986).

It is possible to present a simple example of how the relation of these two features to increasing density can combine to influence the productivity of a pheasant population. Einarsen (1942) recorded the size of the breeding pheasant population on the 160 ha

Protection Island, Washington, following the introduction of a small population of two cocks and six hens in the spring of 1937. These birds flourished on the island and the population grew at an astounding rate (Fig. 8.17). The growth rate slowed as the island became crowded and the population eventually levelled off. At this point the birth and death rates can be considered equal. We can then calculate the growth rate of the population across the whole range of densities. Figure 8.18 shows how the population was at its most productive or growing fastest when at approximately half of its final density. It is at this stage that the number of births most greatly exceeded the number of deaths. If we were to harvest this population the largest sustainable bags would be achieved when the population was held at this level. This can be described as the point of maximum sustainable yield, or MSY.

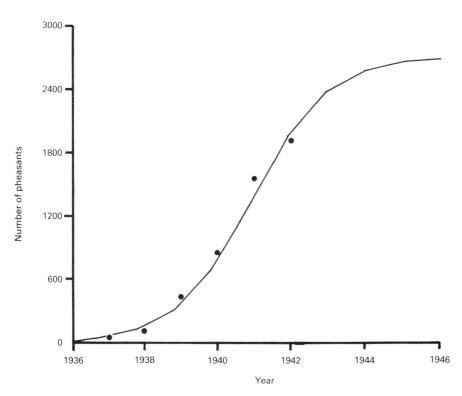

Fig. 8.17 Growth rate of a pheasant population introduced to Protection Island, Washington, in 1936. Logistic growth curve fitted to data (after Einarsen 1942).

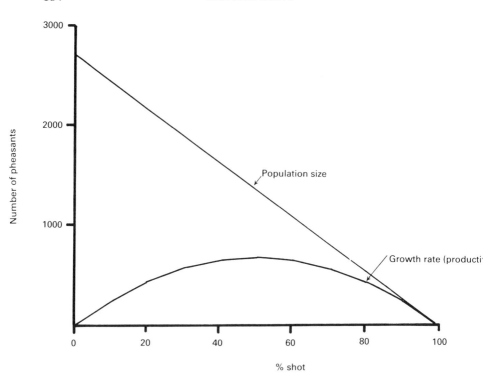

Fig. 8.18 Relationship between the growth rate of the pheasant population introduced to Protection Island, Washington (Einarsen 1942) and population density.

Unfortunately most pheasant populations are not as simple as that on Protection Island and the point of MSY is not so easily determined. Furthermore, the size of most pheasant populations can fluctuate dramatically as a result of changes in chick survival. The uncertainty caused by this variability makes exact determination of the level of hunting necessary to achieve MSY rather meaningless for other than academic purposes and game managers should aim for the more arbitrary optimum sustainable yield, or OSY. This will produce lower bags, but is conservative and does not risk overshooting in years of poor chick survival. Methods used for calculating MSY or OSY for gamebird populations are discussed by Robertson and Rosenberg (1988) while the appropriate values from our Knoll Farm study area and their derivations are described later in this chapter by use of a population model.

One conclusion that can be drawn from this is that leaving hen populations unshot and therefore at a high density may actually decrease the number of chicks produced. As we have discussed it seems that survival and breeding success decline at high densities and that larger long-term bags could be attained by reducing the hen populations to increase their productivity. As such the efforts of many American states to increase breeding populations by banning hen shooting may actually be counterproductive.

On a rather crude basis it is possible to gauge the levels of hunting necessary to achieve MSY by examining bag records to see which hunting pressures have resulted in declines in subsequent bags. This is an unsatisfactory approach as any declines may be simply due to poor breeding seasons or other random fluctuations.

A number of American states have allowed hen shooting for trial periods to examine the effects on the bag. In Wisconsin two seasons where 50–60% of the hens were shot lead to subsequent declines in the bag compared with neighbouring states where hens were protected (Wagner *et al.* 1965). The implication from this is that hens could not sustain a harvest of this magnitude. Similarly, Erikson *et al.* (1951) reports that hen kills of over 33% in Minnesota led to declines while Ginn (1955) reached a similar conclusion when 20–28% of Indiana hens were killed. In California, Harper (1960) found no evidence of detrimental effects on the long-term bag when an average of 16% of the hens were shot.

Use of these studies suggests that hen shooting of approximately 20% or over leads to a decline in subsequent bags and therefore exceeds MSY. It must be stressed that this is an unreliable approach to the problem. It is interesting to note that if the illegal hen kill in these states is in the range of 15–20% then banning hen shooting, while not making sense from the point of view of maximising the bag, may actually succeed in restricting the hen bag to near MSY, the ideal situation. It could be that American bans on hen shooting are right, but for entirely the wrong reasons.

TOWARDS A POPULATION SIMULATION MODEL

A model is basically a means of expressing verbally or mathematically a series of relationships which describe certain biological events, such as the increase, decrease or fluctuation about an equilibrium level, of a population. For the purpose of this chapter we shall describe the use of a 'dynamic-statistical' type constructed from the series of data presented in previous chapters of this book. The equations given in the following paragraphs are merely to aid those who specifically wish to use such models in their own work. For other readers we intend that equations can be skipped without hindering the understanding of our main conclusions. Further details of the modelling are given by Hill and Carter (1988).

There can be no doubt that models which describe either an ecological system or a population of a species which is part of that system are gaining popularity. Jorgensen (1986) states that the application of models to ecological problems 'is almost compulsory if we want to understand the function of such a complex system as an ecosystem'. It is very difficult and time-consuming to study the many components within the system, together with their interrelations, without the use of a model as a means of synthesis.

Ecological models have been used as instruments in the design of surveys of complex systems as well as to reveal weaknesses in our current knowledge so that future research might be planned. They have also been used to test scientific hypotheses by simulating an expected distribution of numbers of individuals etc., which can then be compared with the observed. In general models have become useful tools to the ecologist but they are only as robust as the data from which they are built.

Methods and model construction

The model presented here is based on the life cycle of the pheasant population being studied at Damerham in Hampshire, augmented by the chick survival data from the Sussex study (see Chapter 6). Figure 8.19 represents the model diagrammatically. The important relationships for successive stages in the model are described below, together with background information on how the data were collected and collated.

Male overwinter loss

Male pheasants were found to have a higher rate of overwinter loss in years when the population density was high. Such density-

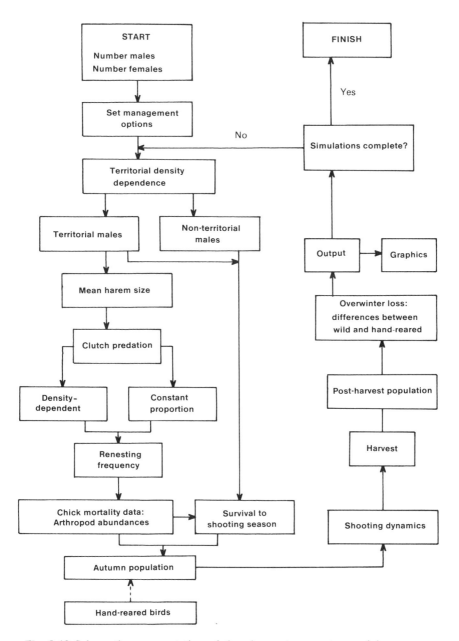

Fig. 8.19 Schematic representation of the pheasant computer model.

dependent mortality is a common feature of many animal populations and is fundamental to the way in which populations respond to shooting. The removal of part of the population by shooting reduces population density and this leads to an increase in the survival and breeding prospects of the remainder. This sort of effect is often termed compensatory survival.

It is possible to describe the relationship between population density and male overwintering loss in mathematical terms where k_m is overwinter loss and M is the density of males in the autumn:

$$k_m = -0.38 + (0.39 \times \log_{10} M)$$

Female overwinter loss

Females were also found to exhibit density-dependent loss during the winter. Overwinter loss of females in the marked population was found to be dependent on the density of females in autumn, and the form of the relationship used in the model is:

$$k_f = -1.464 + (0.762 \times \log_{10} F)$$

where k_f is female overwinter loss and F is the density of females in autumn.

From these data it is impossible to say whether the loss of birds over the winter was due principally to mortality or dispersion out of the study area; undoubtedly both are important. Furthermore, it is probably also true that some birds move onto the study area from the surrounding land. Such immigration is probably especially important when the population on the estate is low relative to neighbouring areas and could conceivably lead to a spring population higher than that found in the autumn. Such immigration is not allowed in the model by constraining the percentage of the autumn population which is lost during the winter to a minimum of 20%. It is important to consider a 'closed' population as an unrealistic number of immigrating birds would give a totally misleading set of harvesting dynamics.

One explanation for the density-dependent nature of pheasant overwinter loss is that it is in response to some limiting resource. The greater the population density, the fewer resources there are to go round. For instance, the density of female groups at

Damerham has been shown to be correlated with the amount of shrub cover (1–2 m height levels) within woodlands in late winter (Chapters 3 and 4). It is therefore possible that some of the density-dependence exhibited is caused by females responding to the limited availability of cover in late winter and early spring.

Male territory establishment

As we have shown, male pheasants are highly territorial and they defend harems of females. At Damerham the number of territorial males remained relatively constant in the five years of study. The proportion of the male population remaining non-territorial in the spring was positively correlated with the size of the population in the previous autumn, including the number of poults released that summer (see Chapter 3). This density-dependent effect means that if there are only a certain number of breeding resources (in this case territory sites) to be shared out, then as the number of males competing for them increases the proportion of the male population unable to obtain a territory also increases.

The relationship describing the loss of males from the breeding population (k_{mb}) in terms of the increase in non-territoriality with an increase in spring male density (Mb) is of the form:

$$k_{mb} = -1.547 + (1.049 \times \log_{10} Mb)$$

Nest success

In the model, nest success is initially kept constant (46%) as there are no data as yet to indicate that the proportion of nests destroyed by predators is greater at high nest density. Pheasants have the capacity to renest successively after the loss of first nests and renesting is included in the model. However there is evidence from studies of the grey partridge that density-dependent nest loss is one of the main regulation processes, where proportionally more nests are lost at high density than at low density (Potts 1986). Extremes for the pheasant of 30% loss at low density and

85% loss at high density (when predators are not controlled) are incorporated into the model using a positive logistic equation:

$$Pn = \frac{85}{1 + e^{3.75 - (0.0455\,F)}}$$

where Pn is the percentage of nests lost at female density F. Both constant nest success and that generated by the above density-dependent term are compared with respect to the differences they cause to the effects of shooting, and when the best long-term harvest can be achieved.

Chick survival

Pheasant chicks are dependent on insects for survival during the first two to three weeks of life (Hill 1985) and in Chapter 6 we showed that where insects are few, chicks range over large areas and suffer heavier mortality than where insects are abundant. Pheasant chick survival has been recorded annually on the Sussex study area since 1969 (Potts 1986) during which period it has averaged $37.3 \pm 2.9\%$. This figure is used unless stated otherwise. To examine long-term changes in the national pheasant population it is also necessary to have an estimate of pheasant chick survival going back to 1961 to coincide with the data on rearing and pheasant bags obtained from the National Game Census. Data on partridge chick survival are available from the Sussex study for this period and as pheasant and grey partridge chick survival are closely correlated each year ($r = 0.61$, $P<0.001$) for 1969–1986 it is possible to extrapolate the survival of the pheasants, for the period 1961–1969, from the relationship:

$$S_p = 0.177 + (0.544 \times S_g)$$

where S_p is percentage pheasant chick survival and S_g is the corresponding value for grey partridges.

Summer survival

Survival rates in the summer were assumed to be different between the two sexes and two age categories (young and old). The survival values used were: territorial males = 0.9; non-territorial males = 0.7; adult females = 0.6; immatures (<one year) = 0.9. The lower survival rate for adult females was attributable to predation on the nest by foxes. These data were also incorporated into the model.

Hand-rearing

We showed in Chapter 7 that the number of pheasants reared and released on shooting estates in Britain has almost trebled in the past 25 years, whereas the total number shot has only doubled. Hand-reared birds can suffer heavy mortality immediately after release and before shooting takes place (Robertson 1986), and the subsequent survival of hand-reared birds from one September to the following January was found at Damerham and on Lyons Estate in Ireland to be only 0.52 that of their wild counterparts. Furthermore, from our radiotelemetry studies in which both wild and hand-reared hens were followed through the summer, hand-reared birds suffer much heavier mortality than wild-reared ones. Consequently breeding success is higher for wild hens than hand-reared ones. Both the lower survival and breeding success of the hand-reared birds are incorporated into the model, the former by attributing the density-dependent overwinter loss according to the proportion of the population consisting of hand-reared birds using the equation:

$$Py = \frac{K}{(0.52\ x) + y}$$

where Py is the proportion of hand-reared birds which suffer mortality during the winter, K is the logarithmic value for overwinter loss converted to a proportion, i.e. 10^{-K}, x is the post-shooting wild-bred population and y is the post-shooting hand-reared population. Relative breeding success is incorporated into the model as 0.26 when all of the breeding population consists of hand-reared birds and 1.0 when none are hand-reared.

   In the next chapter we shall use this model to examine the effects of various management techniques, but for the moment we shall just consider the effects of harvesting the population and how the harvest can be manipulated to maximise the yield.

We shall therefore ask the following questions:

(1) What is the effect on the number of birds shot and the size of
    breeding populations at equilibrium densities, caused by in-
    creasing the proportion of the autumn population killed?
(2) Should the sexes be harvested in different ways to maximise
    the yield?

Shooting the population

By increasing the percentage of the autumn population shot in
the model, and calculating the number of birds harvested, the
point of maximum sustainable yield (MSY) can be established.

Unlike monogamous species, where the best strategy is to
shoot almost equal numbers of males and females, pheasants are
polygynous, many females breeding with the same male (Chapter
4), and this can be exploited during the shooting season. A
number of estates shoot only cock pheasants. Others shoot predominantly cocks, only shooting hens early in the season. The
basis for 'cock only' shooting is that a large proportion of the
male population, particularly after large numbers have been
released, remain non-territorial. These consequently have little
or no influence on the productivity of the breeding population, as
we have shown in Chapter 7. Furthermore, as pheasants are
polygynous, one male can fertilise a large number of females.
Studies in America where the males have been heavily shot have
demonstrated that a spring sex ratio of ten hens per cock does
not result in any decreased fertility amongst the hens (Dale 1952)
while studies of captive birds have raised this to 50:1 without ill-
effect. As such we have constrained fertility of the females to
decline only when a sex ratio of 20 hens per cock or greater is
reached – a very conservative estimate.

Since fertility of hens is not related to the abundance of territorial males, except under extreme conditions, we can model the
effects of increasing the proportion of the male population shot,
on both the harvest of males and the size of the non-territorial
male population. We subsequently found that the male population
was much less susceptible to heavy shooting pressure than the
females. The number of territorial males only began to decline

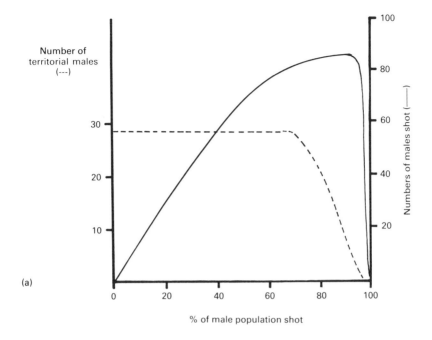

(a)

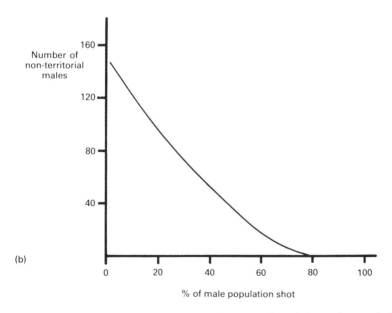

(b)

Fig. 8.20 With an increase in the shooting mortality of the male population the model is used to predict (a) the number of territorial males (broken line) and number of males shot (solid line), and (b) number of non-territorial males.

beyond a shooting mortality of 75% of the male population. This
decline was as a result of the removal of all the non-territorial
males which were subsequently unable to compensate for further
mortality of the territorial males. As shooting mortality was increased the number of non-territorial males in the population
declined (Fig. 8.20). There was no change in the productivity of
females, nor of the total breeding population, as the proportion
of the male population harvested was increased. This continued
until 95% of the males were harvested. At this point their ability
to fertilise all the females declined and productivity began to
drop. The sustainable yield of males was at its peak when 95% of
the males were harvested per year. However, the MSY curve
levels off after taking 80% of the males, further hunting having
little effect on the size of the bag.

What, then, is the appropriate level of harvesting for the females?
For the wild pheasant population being investigated, if nest suc-

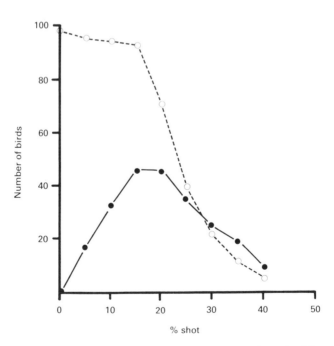

Fig. 8.21 Determination of maximum sustainable yield (MSY) of females based
on the model. Solid line = yield, broken line = breeding female population.

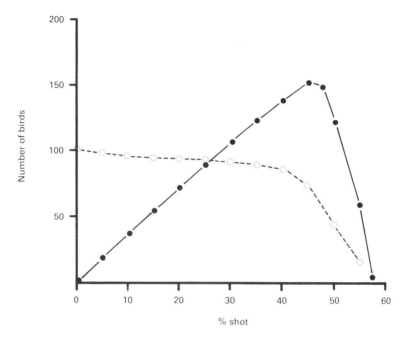

Fig. 8.22 Determination of MSY of females based on the model incorporating density-dependent nest success. Solid line = yield, broken line = breeding female population.

cess is incorporated as a constant (46%), MSY would be achieved by shooting approximately 20% of the autumn hen population and under this level of shooting pressure the breeding population would be reduced to 71% of that without shooting (Fig. 8.21). Optimum conditions of harvest would thus be gained by shooting slightly less than this harvest rate, at the point of optimum sustainable yield (OSY). A similar sustainable harvest plot is given in Fig. 8.22 in which the dynamics of nest success are changed from a constant percentage being destroyed by predators to the hypothetical density-dependent form. The point of MSY is increased to approximately 45% of the autumn population harvested, corresponding to a female breeding population 74% of the size of that without shooting.

Theoretically, therefore, we have two sexes which respond differently to harvesting. On the one hand the male population would appear to be able to compensate for heavy shooting mortality such that the point of maximum sustainable yield is achieved by shooting more than 90% of the autumn population. On the other hand, females should be harvested much more conservatively, probably at around 20% of the autumn population.

It is impossible to 'stockpile' hens due to the density-dependent loss they demonstrate during the winter. Consequently, hens can be shot to increase the bag. The principle of outlawing all hen shooting to conserve breeding stocks is false and a waste of game. However, in areas where rough shooting is the norm and it is therefore difficult to implement a limited hen harvest, a legislative ban may be quite effective in keeping the (illegal) hen kill down to acceptable levels.

9 Management: Past, Present and Future

'That the game department on estates has generally been the least profitable, measured by its expense and losses, will we believe be admitted. Game preservation has, nevertheless, now assumed importance on most estates, and what with the worry and losses connected with landed property in the past, and threatened legislation adverse to owners of land in the future, it has become a question with many landowners to what extent they may abandon agriculture and devote their woods and fields to game and sport, which have always been among the chief inducements to owners to live on their estates, and which, more almost than anything else, has increased the residential value of landed property and kept it up when its agricultural value was going down.' (Simpson 1907)

To provide an overview of management in a historical context, this chapter is divided into five separate sections. The first deals with the ways in which active pheasant management, game-keeping, predator control and hand-rearing have changed since Edwardian times and how they affect pheasant bags. The second section covers woodland management and the provision of other forms of cover. The techniques of woodland management have

197

changed dramatically this century. As markets have changed, coppicing has declined while the area of coniferous woodland has increased. Furthermore, with increasing government subsidies for planting broadleaved trees, to take land out of cereal production, improve the landscape and increase the conservation potential of commercial forestry, the scope for improving the game potential has never been so great.

In the third section we describe how the intensification of cereal production since the last war and increasing pesticide use have led to declines in wild gamebird chick production. The fourth section looks to the future of game management in Britain. The reform of recent subsidies for agriculture, incorporated in the Common Agricultural Policy, provides an opportunity to redress the balance in the countryside and we discuss methods of integrating cereal production and woodland management with game-bird conservation. Lastly we discuss past and present methods of managing pheasants in North America, a continent with many parallels and contrasts to the situation in Britain.

CHANGES IN PHEASANT MANAGEMENT

Decline of the gamekeeper

Between the 1870s and early 1900s, as the need for driven shooting and hand-reared birds accelerated, the number of gamekeepers in Britain increased from about 15 000 to 22 000. During the First World War many keepers went away to fight and either did not return or did not take up their former posts as a result of a change in the economics of the estate. The number in full-time employment fell to about 12 500. After a period of increasing employment during the inter-war years, the Second World War brought a further decline from about 13 500 to fewer than 5000. The numbers since the early 1950s have not recovered and today there are probably fewer than 4500 full-time gamekeepers in Britain.

This decline in numbers is thought to be the result of two factors. After the Second World War, shooting was organised on very different lines. Many tenant farmers rented shooting rights from landowners. Many estates were divided and partly sold off to cover death duties. Entrepreneurial farmers, businessmen, and more lately insurance companies, pension groups and trusts, have taken over many operations. Furthermore, many shoots now organise the estate between themselves by the formation of syndicates. These typically consist of individuals prepared to share the costs of the shoot and to do some 'part-time' keepering. As a result, the services of many professional keepers were no longer required after the war. In addition, methods of hand-rearing pheasants became more intensive. Outdoor broody hen bantams in coops were replaced by indoor incubators and heated brooder units which require much less attention per egg. Hence fewer keepers could rear more and more birds. Not only have these changes led to a decline in the number of keepers but the production of hand-reared birds now accounts for an increasing proportion of a modern gamekeeper's time, with consequences for the extent of predator control and habitat management.

Predator control

During the Edwardian period in Britain the shooting of pheasants on large formal shoots was at its peak. It was exclusive and huge amounts of money were involved. The arrival of the breech loading gun in the 1850s had made driven shooting more attractive and this required large numbers of birds to be driven over the guns by a team of beaters.

In the late 19th and early 20th century many predatory species which are now afforded special protection were controlled because of the effects they were believed to have on game. The vast sums of money spent on the keepering effort and on the poults which were reared on the open field system meant that keepers virtually declared war on species such as the sparrowhawk, goshawk, and buzzard, often using the unselective pole trap. Wild cats in Scotland were dramatically reduced in numbers, and gamekeeper activity has been considered by some to be the prime reason for the restriction in range of some species of predatory birds, particularly the hen harrier.

The Protection of Birds Act (1954) was instrumental in increasing the awareness of the public and those controlling predatory species of the problems of using a broad brush approach in the name of game management. Legal protection was given to many species and as knowledge of the ecology of these predatory species grew, so people were able to be more specific in recognising the main predators of game, and hence advising on the protection of the rest. The 1981 Wildlife and Countryside Act has strengthened the law based on past research findings.

The majority of pheasants are shot in the south-east of Britain and this is where their management is most intensive. Whilst the main reason for the higher numbers of pheasants in the east and south-east is the predominance of lowland arable farms, the two regions appear to differ markedly in the way in which pheasants are managed.

Figure 9.1 shows that the number of pheasants shot per square kilometre in the south-east has been increasing during the period 1961–1985 whilst the number shot in East Anglia has not. Much of the difference would appear to be due to the different levels of hand-rearing in the two areas. In the south-east, rearing has increased dramatically and the numbers shot have risen in response. In the east however, both the levels of rearing and numbers shot have remained relatively stable. The changing emphasis in the south-east has had repercussions for predator control. As shoots come to rely more on reared birds to fuel their sport, so the need to control predators decreases and keepers spend more and more time on the rearing field. So, do the differences in management arising from the increase in hand-rearing coincide with changes in predator populations?

The National Game Census predator records were consulted for average trends in predator numbers on 63 shoots in the south-east and 61 shoots in East Anglia. These can be examined to compare the effects of decreasing the intensity of predator control in the south-east. In the south-east, fox numbers killed per square kilometre have risen dramatically during the period 1961–1985 (Fig. 9.2). In East Anglia, numbers have risen, but the increase has been less dramatic than that in the south-east. Furthermore fewer foxes are killed in East Anglia than the south-east, and this is believed to represent differences in densities of foxes living in these regions.

Stoat numbers killed appear not to differ significantly between the two areas (Fig. 9.3), although it is certain that far more effort

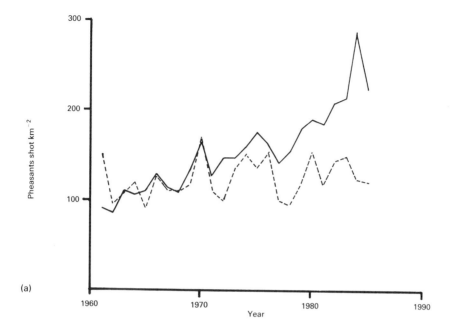

(a)

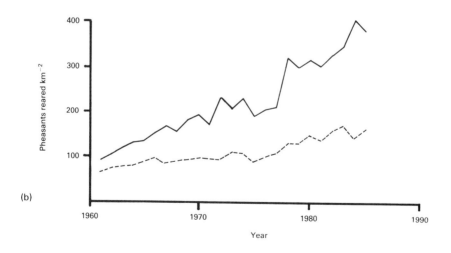

(b)

Fig. 9.1 Pheasants (a) shot and (b) reared per square kilometre in the south-east (solid line) and East Anglia (broken line) respectively from the National Game Census.

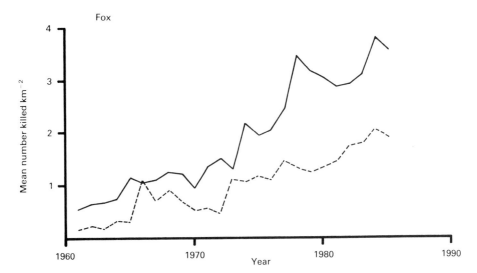

Fig. 9.2 Trends in the mean number of foxes killed on an average of 63 and 61 shoots in the south-east (solid line) and East Anglia (broken line) respectively from the National Game Census.

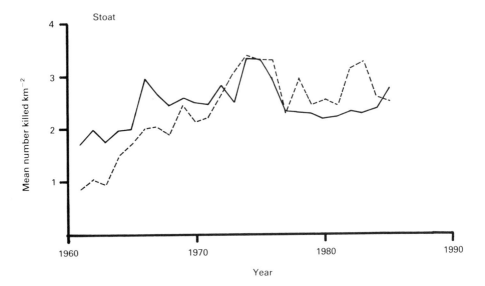

Fig. 9.3 Trends in the mean number of stoats killed on an average of 63 and 61 shoots in the south-east (solid line) and East Anglia (broken line) respectively, from the National Game Census.

is directed towards tunnel trapping stoats in East Anglia than in the south-east.

Corvid populations, as monitored by the National Game Census, reveal some interesting differences between the regions. In the south-east there has been a marked increase in the number of carrion crows killed during 1961–1985 (Fig. 9.4). The picture in East Anglia is somewhat different however, with fewer birds being killed and no increase.

Numbers of magpies killed in the south-east have risen markedly over the same period (Fig. 9.5). In East Anglia however, far fewer magpies are killed, although numbers recorded beyond 1975 do suggest a moderate increase.

Jays are shot on many estates during pheasant drives and as a pest of game. Most jays are shot in winter and higher numbers

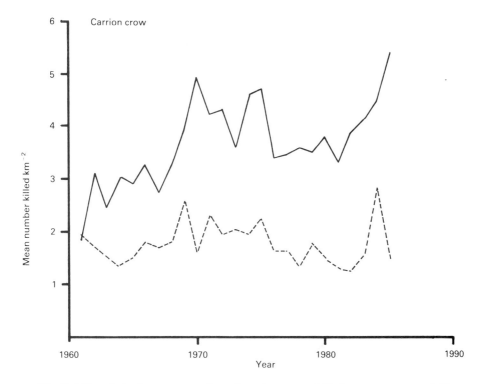

Fig. 9.4 Trends in the mean number of carrion crows killed on an average of 63 and 61 shoots in the south-east (solid line) and East Anglia (broken line) respectively, from the National Game Census.

Fig. 9.5 Trends in the mean number of magpies killed on an average of 63 and 61 shoots in the south-east (solid line) and East Anglia (broken line) respectively, from the National Game Census.

are shot in 'influx' years which are related to failure of the acorn crop in Scandinavian countries and the immigration of continental birds. One such influx occurred in 1983 and was well documented by a rise in the numbers of jays shot that winter. Whilst numbers of jays shot in East Anglia are significantly lower than in the south-east there have been no significant increases or decreases in numbers killed in either region (Fig. 9.6). This suggests that the population is stable, although the winter atlas suggests an increase has occurred since the 1940s (Lack 1986).

The final corvid killed in any numbers is the jackdaw. Declines in numbers shot have been experienced in both the south-east and East Anglia, although numbers killed appear to have increased during the early 1980s in the south-east region (Fig. 9.7).

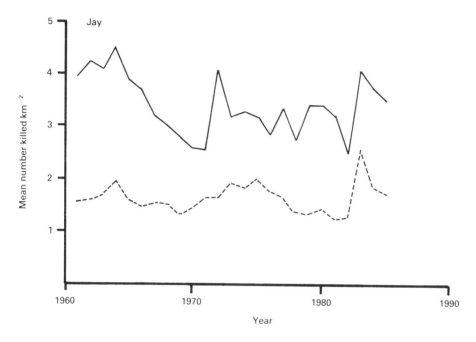

Fig. 9.6 Trends in the mean number of jays killed on an average of 63 and 61 shoots in the south-east (solid line) and East Anglia (broken line) respectively, from the National Game Census.

So, in general the numbers of predators killed per unit area are lower in East Anglia than in the south-east and in the latter area there have been substantial increases in a number of species. Gamekeeper effort is certainly higher in East Anglia and so the lower numbers killed probably indicate lower populations of most of these species. Similarly, the rises observed in the south-east cannot be attributed to increased keeper effort and must reflect real changes in species density. These increases coincide with rises in the levels of hand-rearing and declines in keeper effort towards predator control. It is tempting to suggest that these are cause and effect but this obviously requires a much more thorough study. Many other factors are likely to be responsible for increases or decreases in predator populations of interest to gamekeepers however, and agricultural changes in particular may have an over-riding effect. East Anglian farms are often larger, with bigger fields, fewer hedges and less permanent cover than those in the

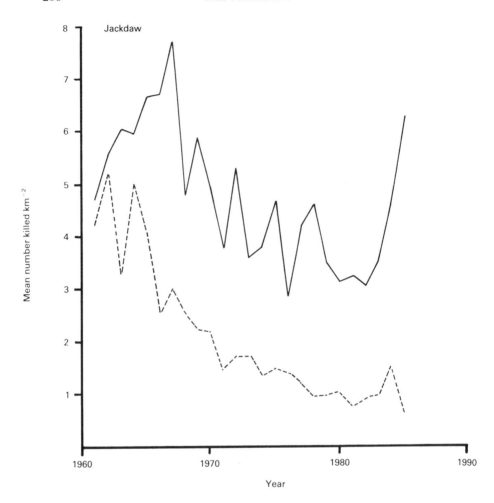

Fig. 9.7 Trends in the mean number of jackdaws killed on an average of 63 and 61 shoots in the south-east (solid line) and East Anglia (broken line) respectively, from the National Game Census.

heavily wooded south-east and this will also influence the numbers and changes outlined above.

Hand-rearing and effects on productivity

We described in Chapter 7 how the numbers of pheasants reared and released on shooting estates in Britain have almost trebled in the past 25 years, whereas the total numbers shot have not increased at the same rate. We found that the survival of hand-reared birds from one winter to the next is only slightly over half that of their wild-reared counterparts. Furthermore, radiotelemetry studies through the summer revealed that hand-reared birds suffer much higher mortality than wild-reared ones. With the current trend towards releasing more and more pheasants each year it is important to determine the long-term effects on the productivity of the population. In order to look at this we shall use the population model developed in the previous chapter.

The model was used to simulate the effects of releasing an increasing number of pheasants for shooting, both on the average number of young raised to fledging age, and on the percentage of the breeding female population comprising hand-reared birds. The model predicted that as the number of pheasants released was increased per unit area, the productivity of the breeding population would steadily decline to stabilise at a lower value (Fig. 9.8). The model also predicted that an increase in the

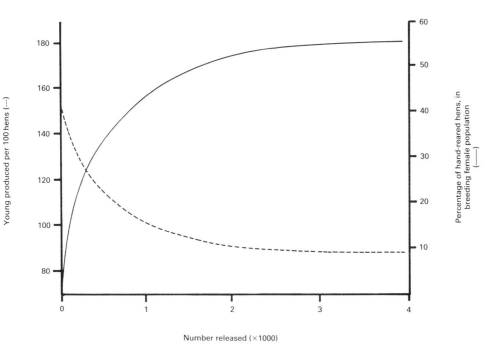

Fig. 9.8 Decline in the number of young produced by 100 hens (dashed line) and the increase in the breeding female population comprising hand-reared birds (solid line), as the number of birds released on the typical estate is increased.

number released would lead to an increase in the percentage of
the breeding female population consisting of hand-reared birds,
reaching a plateau of some 57% of the breeding numbers. This
simply reflects the number of hand-reared birds surviving into
their second year reaching an equilibrium. This example is in the
absence of shooting. If shot, the proportion of juvenile hand-
reared birds breeding reaches an equilibrium at a higher level.

This very general approach simulated only an increase in the
numbers of hand-reared birds released on a year-to-year basis.
Of much more importance from both economic and ecological
points of view are the longer term effects of rearing a constant
number of pheasants on an area. The model was used to investigate the effect of releasing 2000 per year on the Damerham
study area on the productivity of the wild-breeding population.
The model predicted a significant downward trend in productivity
occurring over a seven-year period (Fig. 9.9).

A further prediction from the model concerns the effects of
shooting pressure on the percentage of the breeding female population consisting of hand-reared birds, following the annual release
of 400 poults per square kilometre as described above. As the
proportion of the autumn population shot was increased, hand-
reared birds made a greater contribution to subsequent breeding
populations (Fig. 9.10). This is because although increased shooting rates place greater pressure on both hand-reared and wild
birds, the hand-reared birds do not suffer the consequences of
overshooting as their numbers can always be replenished by further
rearing. Wild birds, on the other hand, must rely on survivors to
produce sufficient chicks to form next year's population. The
increasing proportion of hand-reared birds in the breeding population also leads to fewer fledged young, further reducing the wild
population (Hill and Robertson 1987b).

Thus, rearing decreases the productivity of the breeding population by diluting the number of wild hens. This is a progressive
effect and is exacerbated by increasing shooting pressure. How
important have these effects been in determining the size of the
annual pheasant bag?

Using the simulation model, the data on the numbers of birds
released per year from the National Game Census and estimates
of annual pheasant chick survival, as described earlier, it is possible to model the changes in the pheasant bag since 1961. The

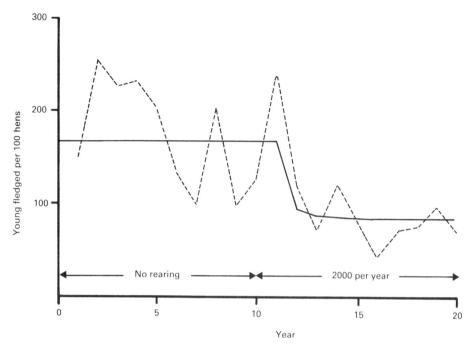

Fig. 9.9 Predictions from the pheasant model of the long-term effects of releasing hand-reared pheasants on the productivity of the hen population on the Damerham study area. In this example no birds were released during the first ten years, subsequent to this 2000 birds were released per year. The broken line simulates the expected changes in productivity including a random element to approximate year to year changes in chick survival; the solid line represents the same data but without this variable element.

model provides reasonable predictions of the observed changes in the British pheasant bag since 1961 (Fig. 9.11).

It is also possible to predict what would have happened to the British pheasant population had there not been any annual restocking (Robertson and Hill in press). It appears that pheasant chick survival has not been sufficient to sustain the wild population and it would, in the absence of rearing, have declined in a similar manner to the grey partridge (Potts 1986). Alternatively, if hand-reared birds were of an equal standard to wild birds, both in terms of survival and breeding success, the bags would have been almost twice as large. Clearly then the population is heavily dependent on hand-reared birds to sustain the bag, but these

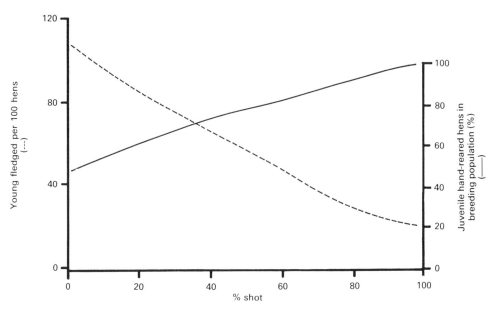

Fig. 9.10 Predictions from the pheasant model of the effects of increasing the percentage of the population shot per year on the percentage of hand-reared birds in the breeding population (solid line) and the number of young produced by 100 hens (dashed line) at Damerham when 800 birds were released per year.

birds make a much smaller per capita contribution to natural productivity than their wild counterparts.

Finally, it is possible to predict the effects of a hypothetical cessation of hand-rearing. If no more birds were reared after 1985 then the population would crash (Fig. 9.12). Thus, although the pheasant population status appears sound, this in fact only reflects the continual input of large numbers of hand-reared birds.

If estates were to cease rearing, for whatever reason, it is essential to recognise that a population crash may result. Under these circumstances they would not be able to shoot appreciable numbers of birds until their stock of wild hens had recovered. Understandably, many estates are reluctant to take this step. One possible solution may be to rear only males and shoot only this sex, which would allow the stock of wild hens to recover while still allowing large-scale shooting. Once the stock of wild hens has recovered then they could also be harvested, albeit lightly, as discussed in Chapter 8. This sounds fine in theory but remains to be tested on a significant scale in the wild.

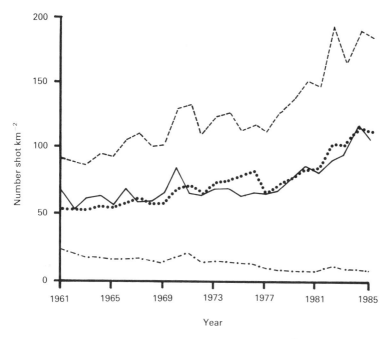

Fig. 9.11 The observed numbers of pheasants shot per km² on estates in Britain since 1961 as recorded by the National Game Census (solid line) compared with the predicted bag from the pheasant model (dotted line). This graph also includes two simulations. The upper broken line is the predicted bag if hand-reared birds survived and bred as well as do their wild counterparts. The lower broken line is the predicted bag had there never been any rearing.

Many shoots only exist because of hand-rearing, but the move back to more traditional management on many others may not be far away. Certainly the implications of our findings regarding the effects of hand-rearing on the sustainability of the wild population should lead to a more sympathetic view of wild-reared pheasants and their management.

WOODLAND MANAGEMENT AND THE PROVISION OF WINTER COVER

Until driven shooting was developed little attention was paid to woodland as a habitat for pheasants. As the demand for more birds increased so too did the attention paid to designing and planting coverts specifically to hold and 'show' birds.

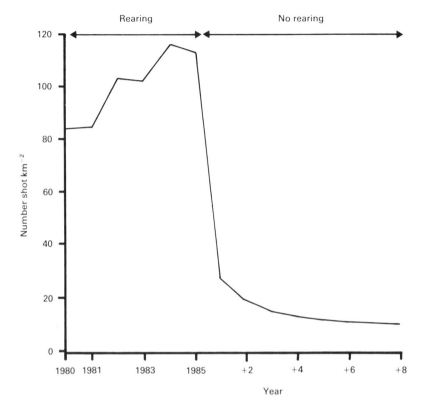

Fig. 9.12 The predictions from the pheasant model as to the effect of a total cessation of pheasant rearing in 1985 on the numbers shot per km^2 on National Game Census estates.

The requirements of pheasants and the ways in which woods can be managed to their benefit have long been recognised. John Simpson wrote his famous book *Game and Game Coverts* in 1907 and many of his comments are as relevant today as they were then. We shall use extracts from his text to illustrate how little things have changed.

'It is not often necessary to create game coverts from the beginning because on most estates of any extent old existing woods may be converted on the same principle that it is proposed to form new coverts....' (Simpson 1907)

At the turn of the 19th century woods and coverts were planted in groups, each covert being small in size. There was considerable interest in silviculture at this time and attention was paid to producing timber from the coverts and woods which could either be used on the farm or sold for profit. Coverts were arranged in such a way as to secure protection from cold and provide shelter for birds.

'It is better that every wood and copse on the estate should be a covert, and detached coverts should be as numerous and as widely distributed as extent and circumstances will permit, and should extend to the limits of the estate.' (Simpson 1907)

These thoughts are still relevant in today's economic climate. Farmers nowadays are faced with similar problems to those of their forefathers of nearly a century ago. The conflicts between the usual methods of producing timber and pheasant shooting still exist and yet, in reality, compromises are just as possible as they were then, even though it is often the case that neither interest acknowledges the requirements of the other:

'Whether owners choose to combine timber with game preservation or not, it is right to state here that that may be done successfully, and the idea entertained by both British foresters and gamekeepers that the dense continental system of forestry is incompatible with game preservation is a delusion, and arises from a misconception of the facts. Sacrificing the one for the other is not here contemplated where such a course can be avoided. Not only may dense timber crops be combined with game preservation but young plantations up to twenty or thirty years of age are amongst the best of game coverts themselves, and where there is a regular succession of woods of various ages not much else is required; but such a state of things rarely exists, because the forestry and game departments are usually in conflict.' (Simpson 1907)

This provides us with a unique insight into the attitudes of keepers and foresters of over 80 years ago. They recognised the value of young conifer plantations and that their attractiveness to pheasants declines with age, also that it was just as easy to grow timber on small areas as on large ones. During this period, the value of mixed farming was also acknowledged for its benefits to pheasants, just as today we believe that mixed farming has more wildlife importance than our fashionable and supposedly efficient 'economic' monocultures.

At the end of the 19th century, coppicing was still a common form of woodland management. However, some conflicts with game production did occur largely because of the size of the coppicing operations. Generally, larger blocks were coppiced than were considered most suitable for pheasants. However, the decline of coppicing was already under way by 1907.

'Coppice is now practically worthless and ought really to come under the head of Waste Lands. The question for owners in the meantime is what to do with such waste areas, and we can suggest nothing better than conversion into game preserves, which would be neither difficult nor costly.

'The faults of coppice for shooting purposes, as usually grown, are that it is in too large areas, is usually too dense, and often too high to shoot either through or over, and without roosting trees. Otherwise anything better, in the shape of ready made covert, we have never seen either for fur or feathers. There is always much humus in the ground and myriads of insects and bugs pervade such thickets. Enormous numbers of rabbits can exist in dense coppice, but in order to shoot them or pheasants in such places it is necessary that broad glades should be cut out in every direction for the guns, leaving the coppice in blocks not too large to work.' (Simpson 1907)

We shall describe in a later section of this chapter how history repeats itself, and how management prescriptions today mirror those carried out over 80 years ago.

Woodland removal and dereliction

Since the turn of the century there have been three major ways in which woodlands and their management have changed. First, the decline in woodmanship and markets for produce has dramatically reduced the area of active coppice and led to many instances of woodland dereliction. Figure 9.13 shows the decline in area of active coppice since 1890 to the present time, together with the almost exponential rise in total woodland area. This is associated with the vast increase in the planting of conifers and the conversion of native broadleaved woodland to coniferous forestry. The third category is the direct loss of woodland as a result of grubbing

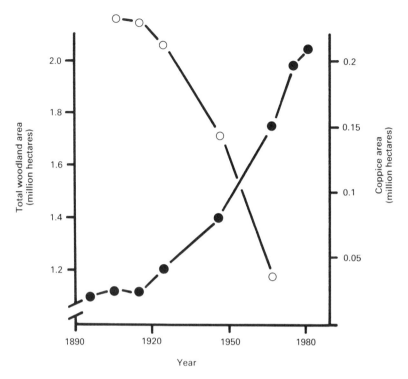

Fig. 9.13 Changes in the total area of woodland, mixed, deciduous and conifer-ous (closed symbols), and the area of coppice (open symbols) in Britain. (Redrawn from Peterken 1981.)

out for agriculture, largely in order to provide more land for arable crops.

Woodland dereliction, in which the felling of standard trees, natural regeneration, broadleaved planting and coppicing have declined, can eventually give rise to high forest woodlands. These can have a high diversity of fauna but are poorer in terms of ground flora than coppiced woodlands, and are not good for pheasants because of the lack of shrubs. The decline in coppicing is correlated with a loss of an ancient market for coppice products (Rackham 1978). The firewood trade was undercut by an ex-panding railway system at the end of the 19th century, due to which it became cheaper to distribute coal from the coal fields to the more widely dispersed towns and villages, which had pre-viously relied on coppice faggots for fuel. Sheep farming also declined in many areas and the demand for hurdles was reduced. So the mosaic pattern of different aged blocks or coupes of coppice began to disappear between the two World Wars and this probably had significant effects on the pheasant holding capacity of many individual estates.

Between one third and one half of all ancient woodlands in existence in 1945 have been lost to agriculture or, more commonly, converted to conifer plantations (Rackham 1978). In 1979 the Nature Conservancy Council wrote 'the active conversion of broadleaved woodlands to conifers, combined with their clearance for agriculture and other uses, has now reached the stage where continued existence of semi-natural broadleaved woodland outside nature reserves is seriously threatened in many parts of Britain'. The Countryside Review Committee in 1975 showed that 30% of woods of less than 2.5 acres (1 ha) had been cleared away during the period 1947−72. These woodlands were of exactly the right size to maximise densities of pheasants. In the past the government has aided such clearance by providing 20−30% of the cost of their removal in the name of agricultural improvement.

The exact loss of broadleaved woodland remains difficult to assess. In 1947 the Forestry Commission undertook a woodland census, which was repeated in 1980. Sue Everett, whilst a member of the Chief Scientists Team of NCC, carried out a detailed comparison of woodland areas based on the two censuses. She revealed that England as a whole has suffered a loss of 10% of the 1947 broadleaved woodland area, Wales a 20% loss, and Scotland a staggering 44% loss. The real differences are undoubtedly greater because of inadequacies in the censusing techniques and their comparability. For example, the 1947 survey only included woods greater than 5 acres (2 ha) in size whereas the 1980 survey only included all woods greater than half an acre (0.25 ha).

To a large extent the conversion of broadleaved woodland to conifers is a result of the attractive tax incentives and grants provided by the government. In 1977 financial institutions bought more than 10% of all the land sold in England and Wales (Shoard 1980), and such organisations are likely to pursue profit more single-mindedly than are gentleman farmers. Conifer woods also yield money faster, and hence more often, than those of broadleaves, irrespective of the tax benefits offered.

When a wood is 'coniferised' the ground vegetation may flourish for a few years although the species composition will be different from that of the ancient wood it has replaced. During this time it will provide excellent cover for pheasants. However, when conifers grow up they shade out the ground flora, leaving bare ground which is very unattractive to pheasants. Consequently the conversion of broadleaved woods to conifers is detrimental to pheasants after the conifers have established themselves.

Hedgerow loss

We are now familiar with the descriptions of the loss of hedgerows from the British landscape. Whilst hedgerow removal had probably has significant deleterious effects on grey partridge populations which use them during territory establishment and nesting (Potts 1986), their value to pheasants is more difficult to interpret. Hedgerow nesting is not essential to pheasants – they will nest in copses, woods, and cereal fields, as we discussed in Chapter 5. Nevertheless the removal of hedgerows represents the loss of permanent cover which is often used, albeit suboptimally, during the winter and by males during territory establishment. Hedgerows also provide areas which are driven on smaller shooting days and are the 'bread and butter' of the rough shoot.

Estimates of the rate of removal vary between regions of the country. The worst rates of loss between the Second World War and the present time have been in the cereal growing regions of eastern England. Here 'parish after parish, particularly in richly hedged ancient landscapes of Suffolk and north Essex, now has half the hedges that were present in 1945' (Rackhan 1978). The peak rate of loss in Britain in 1965 was equivalent to 15000 miles (24000 km) per year. Much of the west and north of England still have a relatively complete hedge system but the quality of these is often very poor because of a lack of management or damage by livestock.

Nevertheless, pheasants thrive exceedingly well where hedges and woods are scarce – for example in the fenlands of East Anglia. As we have stated previously the network of ditches and dykes appears to be the key to high pheasant densities in this region. In effect of course the ditches can be regarded as 'inverted' hedges, providing similar shelter and habitat during winter and breeding seasons.

Current methods of providing cover

The profitability of agriculture has undoubtedly deterred land-owners from many of the sorts of woodland management ben-eficial for wild pheasants. As a second option, quicker methods for establishing a shoot or for attempting to hold hand-reared birds have been developed. These include the use of gamecrops, usually of little agriculture value, which are planted for the ben-efits they give to pheasants and partridges, and the planting of 'instant' spinneys. Finally, some woodland management is carried out for pheasants at the present time, involving ride creation and maintenance, removal or thinning of standards, and the encour-agement of ground and shrub flora. We shall outline these below.

(a) The use of game crops

An increasingly wide range of game crops are planted on estates in order to 'hold' birds through the winter period, to provide them with food, and to create habitats from which they can be driven on shooting days. This management practice is not restric-ted to Britain — many parts of the United States provide 'residual cover' for pheasants, and many eastern European countries also plant these crops.

Game crops are typically planted to provide cover. Kale, canary grass, artichokes, mustard and fodder radish are all cover crops, whereas maize, buckwheat, sunflower, tic beans, millet, wheat and barley are all planted both for cover and the food they can provide. Maize, millet and sunflower only grow well in the southern parts of Britain; the harsher northern climate limits their development.

The size of the area planted varies according to the amount of land available to be given over to the shooting interests of the estate, but a series of half hectare blocks is typical. The money the farm loses as a consequence of planting game crops instead of cereals etc., can often be partially compensated for by a reduction in the amount of food artificially provided for the birds.

The siting of the game crop is an important part of present−day pheasant management. On open landscapes such as downland, game crops provide patches of habitat in a situation where cover is vital if pheasants are to be held in any numbers. The area alongside a thick hedge or shelterbelt is often chosen and in many cases this is because the shading effects reduce the productivity of the head-land cereal crop and so the farmer has less to lose.

In terms of their growth patterns there are essentially three types of game crops. Annuals, such as maize and kale, require a full growing season and are sown in April, May or June. Perennials, like artichokes, are also sown in April or May, producing new growth each year without having to be sown annually. Catch crops such as mustard are sown after the harvest with the aim of giving them sufficient time to develop and provide some cover before the onset of winter.

A number of agricultural crops provide cover for pheasants during the course of the year. Where dairy and beef herds are farmed areas of kale are widely used. In sheep country fields of turnips are likewise important. Game crops which are left to reseed in successive years are perhaps most heavily used by pheasants at all times of the year. They can contain a diversity of broadleaved weeds as a result of remaining unsprayed with herbicide. During the summer months these crops with their associated weeds can have a large invertebrate community which will improve the survival of pheasant chicks. Some broods which have been radiotracked in this type of habitat on the Damerham study area had much smaller home ranges and survived better than others feeding in sprayed cereal fields where insect food was less plentiful.

After winter frosts and snowfall the majority of game crops lose their value for pheasants. Frosts kill off the remaining green parts of the plant and snowfall flattens crops so removing their value as cover. As a result the provision of more permanent cover is vital to the maintenance of a pheasant population after the shooting season. In the fenlands cover is provided by perennial reed vegetation within ditches. Woods and spinneys are not as necessary in these landscapes although, according to an ongoing study, they are used a great deal when they are present. In order to retain pheasants into the breeding season many estates, particularly those on open countryside such as downland, have integrated 'instant spinneys' into the landscape, thereby increasing the total area of permanent cover.

(b) The instant spinney

Trees take a long time to grow. For the shoot this means a long wait before cover is established which can hold pheasants. In order to speed up the process game crops are often planted amongst small spinneys during their establishment. The crop provides a habitat which will be used by pheasants within one year of planting, and also creates a more sheltered environment which may facilitate better growth and development of the trees.

In the spinney, trees are fitted with individual guards, and a hedge around the perimeter of the planting gives extra shelter. The hedge species often used is *Lonicera nitida* which is fast growing and establishes quickly. However, as we shall discuss later, there are important conflicting ideas with regard to the use of such non-natives in the establishment of permanent woody cover in the countryside. Its value as a quick growing species, providing the term 'instant' to the spinney design, is acknowledged, but its value to conservation, even though it must provide shelter and nest-sites to other non-game species, is thought to be small. Its widespread use on pheasant estates has caused concern and yet little is known of its ecology in this country.

(c) Woodland management

The planting of new woodlands and the management of existing ones has become much more important in Britain in recent years as a result of new initiatives and grants following the Forestry Commission's Broadleaved Woodland Grant Scheme launched in October 1985. Whilst this has been seen by many to fall short of its conservation objectives it is still a step in the right direction.

Changing the emphasis from conifers on the one hand to broad-leaved plantations on the other is seen to be an advantageous move for wildlife and landscaping although, in the case of beech plantations, there may not be such significant differences in wildlife potential.

The pheasant is the main game species in Britain today, and looks set to remain so for many years to come. Woodland planting requires a great deal of foresight; those planting hardwoods for pheasants today will probably never see the fruits of their labours. This 'Capability Brown' approach to future landscape features has prevented a more rapid uptake of the Forestry Commission's initiative. Farmers and landowners often prefer to plant species which yield them game habitat within a shorter time period than those concerned only with native broadleaves. Even so, demand for 'pheasant woodlands' is increasing in Britain. In the United States, with the apparent lack of woodland habitat in many areas, more emphasis is placed on the role of agriculture in determining pheasant numbers. Old fields with weedy growth and shrubby edges provide the infrastructure to the landscape which in Britain would probably be lost if remaining woodlands were removed. We describe this in more detail towards the end of this chapter.

The contribution that shooting interests make to retaining and enhancing woodlands purely for pheasants is difficult to determine, save only to state that in many countries it is regarded by conservationists as considerable. On the Hardingham Estate in Norfolk the owner has more than doubled the area of woodland using a mixture of mostly native broadleaves and conifers, and one member of the Game Conservancy advisory team has been involved in the planting of some 4000 hectares (10 000 acres) of small woods for pheasants over a 30-year period. The importance of the retention of existing woodland is thought to be greater, but we shall return to this topic in the final chapter.

Current woodland designs on a larger scale than the instant spinney described earlier use *Lonicera nitida* hedges and a mixture of shrub species in belts throughout the planting. It has been suggested (McCall 1985, Gray 1986) that hawthorn is the more natural alternative. In conservation terms hawthorn is superior to *Lonicera nitida*. The woods are structured in cross-section by having a graded shrubby edge in terms of height, the tree species being of taller varieties the further from the edge they are planted. This is expected to create the best conditions of shelter conducive to holding pheasants in winter.

We have shown in an earlier chapter how pheasants are birds of woodland edges. Much of woodland management for pheasants is concerned with increasing the length of edge per unit area. The creation of rides is an important feature of present-day woodland management for pheasants, typically shrubby edged rides with a grassy flora in the centre of large woods. The grassy rides provide extra edges for holding birds during the winter and also feeding habitat for broods, being inhabited by a large invertebrate community as we described earlier.

Conifers such as Lawson's cypress, Douglas fir or Norway spruce are often planted in rows amongst young broadleaves, thereby acting as a nurse crop, and by their faster growth, protect the young broadleaves during the first few years of establishment. They are also invaluable in providing early shelter for game. After ten years or so these are removed and sold for poles etc., the broadleaves and associated shrubs are then managed for timber in the long term and shooting in the shorter term.

The planting of new woodlands described above is only part of current woodland management aimed at encouraging and providing better habitats for pheasants. In Britain there remain large tracts of derelict or neglected woodland which would benefit greatly from management. For example, the demand for coppice products is, today, very small compared to 100 years ago. Nowadays the majority of the old traditionally coppiced woodlands remain in an unmanaged state. Traditional mixed hardwoods which might comprise forest trees such as oak, ash, beech, hornbeam or sweet chestnut often have an understorey of coppice. Hazel coppice is widespread in much of the south of England while in Kent and Sussex hornbeam and sweet chestnut predominate. Hornbeam coppice was used for charcoal and sweet chestnut today is still coppiced for fencing stakes. In certain places local demand for firewood has rekindled coppice management, particularly where ash, hornbeam and sycamore are concerned. Increasing demand for fuel for wood-burning stoves means that larger blocks of woodland are now being managed. A further cause for the increasing demand has been the exhaustion of elm following Dutch elm disease. Whilst some of these areas of woodland are still managed traditionally the extent is much less than that of a few decades ago. A small number of estates use coppicing as a means of creating a diverse age structure for pheasants, although some only 'skylight' the woodland by removing some standards together with some patches of derelict coppice. Large clearances produce too big an area of regrowth when the ground vegetation does recover and so, for pheasants at least, smaller blocks or coupes are cut than would have been the case for fuel many years ago. Circles of 20−25 m diameter are spread at intervals throughout the wood, the aim being to produce manageable clumps of well distributed cover and shelter. Tops and side branches are often left in piles to create further cover. They can also provide a framework for shrubs such as bramble which grow in the improved light conditions. When left covering the coppice stools they can act as protection from deer browsing on the growing shoots. Clearance of slightly larger blocks allows planting up with broadleaves using tree guards. This rehabilitation of broadleaved woodland ought to be a more important part of the role of the shoot.

CHANGES IN AGRICULTURE

Pesticides

During the Second World War the demand for food and the pressure placed on farmers to produce it soared. The government's policy at the time had the aim of high and increasing yields from crops, primarily cereals. At the same time large amounts of money were spent on research geared towards advancing our knowledge of means of fertilising the crops and protecting them from pests.

There are three broad categories of pesticides: herbicides, insecticides and fungicides. Herbicides are used at three stages of cultivation. First, they may be used to 'clean' the ground between harvest and cultivation. This will tend to remove early winter food supplies for pheasants and other species such as buntings and finches. Second, they are used to clean the ground before

sowing so as to enable the crop to grow unhindered from competitive weeds. Third, herbicides may be applied at the early
stages of crop growth, i.e. at post-emergence. This practice
eliminates competitive weeds at crop establishment.

The second category of pesticide is the insecticide group. They
can be used as seed dressings and as sprays at any stage of crop
growth. Although most insecticides are only used with the inten-
tion of killing specific groups of insect, many have more general
effects and can kill many non-target species. The third category,
fungicides, take the form of fungicidal seed dressings or, more
recently, as foliar applications to control diseases in the developing
crop. Furthermore, many farmers spray on a routine basis, re-
gardless of the presence of economically significant damage.

Pesticides can affect pheasants and partridges in three ways.
First there is direct poisoning either from the birds ingesting the
product or by coming into contact by other means. Potts (1986),
however, shows that losses caused by direct poisoning are negligible. Secondly, sub-lethal effects of pesticides can cause physiological changes in reproduction thereby reducing productivity.
Eggshell thinning in some raptors, caused by an accumulation of
DDE, a metabolite of DDT, falls into this category, as does
embryo abnormality caused by high levels of pesticides accumulated by the parents. Thirdly, pesticides can affect ecological
changes in the food chain, for example by removing the insects
on which the chicks feed. It is this final effect which we consider
to be the most fundamental problem facing gamebird breeding
success.

Sheail (1985) and Potts (1986) describe the historical changes
in pesticides use and the different types of active ingredients
used. In gamebirds there is little evidence for direct toxicity of
herbicides, insecticides or fungicides, whereas for other species
studied, notably the stock dove which feeds on grain, direct
toxicity was once important (O'Connor and Shrubb 1986).

In Chapter 6 we showed that arthropods are crucial to the
survival of pheasant chicks. Without them, chicks die of starvation. Many herbicides are detrimental because they remove the
food plants on which live the arthropods eaten by pheasant chicks.
At least one fungicide may also have direct insecticidal properties
(Sotherton and Moreby 1984). Potts (1986) has further shown
through long-term monitoring on a number of Sussex estates that
three groups of cereal insects have suffered steep declines in

abundance through the late 1960s to the mid 1980s, including (1) those which feed on weeds growing in fields, (2) polyphagous predators which feed on a wide range of other arthropods, (3) those which feed on fungi. Some insects from each of these groups are eaten by pheasant chicks. The annual period over which pesticides are used has also spread so that weeds and insects come under attack throughout the year. The use of these pesticides therefore has far-reaching implications for game populations. Potts (1986) argues that increased herbicide use has been the main cause of the decline in partridge chick survival in Britain. The trend in pheasant chick survival has been less well documented apart from on the Sussex study area where Potts concentrated his work and in which any decline must have taken place prior to 1970 as it did in the partridge, before these data were collected.

Undersowing, in which a grass or legume is sown with the cereal so as to develop after the harvest, has also declined in popularity. The undersown crop had many important arthropods associated with it, such as sawfly larvae which are favoured food items of both pheasant and grey partridge chicks.

So what of the future? It is unlikely that many new compounds will come on the market (Conway 1982), although the 'convenience use' of cocktails with various constituents will doubtless continue. The reliance of gamebird chicks on insects and the intensive use of pesticides gives cause for concern for the long-term status of wild gamebird populations. Since herbicides do a relatively effective job in removing plants which are hosts to chick food arthropods the future is quite daunting. The only way forward will be to critically review the arable environment in its broadest context. The inclusion of selectively sprayed headlands (Sotherton *et al.* 1985) may alleviate the problem in some areas.

LOOKING TO THE FUTURE

We have described the changing countryside in which wild pheasants have had to take a back seat. Agricultural improvements resulting from technological advances have removed many features of the habitat important to pheasants. However, increasing hand-rearing has masked many of the effects of these changes. Can we therefore learn from the past and from our current knowledge of pheasant ecology? If so, what prescriptions might we make to redress the balance in our countryside?

The research findings described in the previous chapters of this book have pointed to a series of stages in the life cycle of the pheasant at which, with more sympathetic management, their numbers in the wild could be increased with significant beneficial improvements to the way in which we presently view land-use. With the aid of the computer simulation model which we developed in the previous chapter we shall describe the likely effects of improving conditions for wild pheasants. We shall point out the most important management techniques which can improve pheasant productivity and holding capacity, and will then demonstrate how these techniques can be implemented on existing estates in Britain.

Brood rearing habitat

Using the simulation model, we examined the effects of either increasing or decreasing the density of arthropod food items available to chicks during their first three weeks of life. A 60% increase in arthropod density caused chick survival to increase to an average of 52%, whereas a 60% decrease in food caused a decline in chick survival rate to an average of 23%. Table 9.1 shows that improvements in chick survival should lead directly to large increases in autumn numbers as chick mortality is not density-dependent. Consequently improvements in chick

Table 9.1 Model estimates ($\bar{x}\pm$se) of equilibrium populations of pheasants in autumn, in relation to changes in nest success and chick survival (Nos per square kilometre)

	Autumn pheasant density (nos/100 ha)
Observed	130 ± 8
Nest success	
50% increase	220 ± 16
50% decrease	99 ± 5
Chick survival	
60% increase in arthropods	177 ± 8
60% decrease in arthropods	72 ± 8

survival by modifying the availability of arthropod food during the critical first three weeks of a chick's life can significantly increase the number of birds available in the shooting season.

We showed in Chapter 6 that pheasant chicks have a relatively catholic diet. The inclusion of selectively sprayed headlands covering a maximum of 2–6% of the average sized field allows host weed plants, largely broadleaved species, to develop and provide food for arthropods which are then eaten by the chicks. The benefits gained from higher chick survival, producing wild pheasants less likely to suffer predation than costly hand-reared birds (Chapter 7), could tip the balance in favour of conserving these headlands for game.

The agricultural scene is presently in a state of change and as yet we do not know what is to be done with the land surplus to that needed for growing crops. Whether it is destined by government to remain fallow, or to provide a substrate on which to grow trees, or specialist crops (with their own portfolio of pesticides), or to build houses, is still anyone's guess. In the United States old abandoned fields provide excellent conditions for arthropods which pheasants will eat, but only during the early successional stages prior to developing into woodland. It is therefore vital that weedy habitats or field margins are recognised for their value to gamebirds, and that this value influences the chance of such areas being 'set aside'.

Even within intensively managed landscapes there is potential for improving habitats for broods. By cutting the side of grassy woodland rides only in alternate years, for example, many arthropods which are relished by pheasants are encouraged. By contrast, mowing the whole width of the ride will remove this potential habitat and an important food source for chicks.

Woodland management and holding capacity

Within the lowland arable landscape, woods provide pheasants with shelter in the winter and breeding habitats in the spring. Our research has shown that small woods of less than one hectare in size are better than larger woods for holding birds in winter. A series of small woods on the estate will also provide a greater edge to area ratio than one large wood. Consequently at breeding time the availability of more edge enables a greater number of males to gain territories. However, a wood which lacks a shrub layer, such as that created by a dense stand of mature beech, is of little value to pheasants, no matter what its size.

We know that females prefer to use shrubby woodlands in winter and to breed along shrubby edges in early spring. The computer simulation model was used to study the effects of varying the amounts of shrub cover in woodlands on both the number of females remaining to breed and the autumn population size in the subsequent year (Table 9.2). The effect of altering the amount of shrub cover within woodlands was studied by changing the strengths of the density-dependent overwinter loss in females, for we have shown that overwinter loss is higher from habitats with few shrubs and that the holding capacity is greatest for woods with copious shrub cover (Chapter 3). The model showed that relatively small changes to the density-dependence in overwinter loss in response to shrub abundance in woods led to very large percentage changes in both the numbers of females remaining to breed and the autumn population size (Table 9.2). The model therefore demonstrated the potential value of managing habitats to increase the number of breeding females. Alleviation of some

Table 9.2 Effect of changes in the parameters of density dependence (dd) on females surviving the winter and subsequent autumn populations at equilibrium. This simulates the effect of changes in the amount of breeding habitat for females (Nos per square kilometre)

	No. surviving the winter	Autumn population size
Observed	64 ± 4	130 ± 8
Decrease intercept by 30%*	233 ± 14	471 ± 29
Increase intercept by 30%*	18 ± 1	36 ± 2
Decrease strength of dd from 0.762 to 0.6	230 ± 15	465 ± 30
Increase strength of dd from 0.762 to 1.0	22 ± 1	44 ± 2

*This is the intercept of the density-dependent relationship between the number of females in the autumn and the proportion surviving to breed the following spring. A decrease in intercept represents an increase in female survival. Similarly a decrease in the strength of density dependence causes a higher proportion of females remaining to breed at higher densities. This simulates the effect of increasing the amount of shrub cover within woodlands.

of the density-dependence until new 'carrying capacities' are attained could perhaps be achieved by sympathetic woodland management, encouraging shrubs in woods lacking in this feature, together with the resurrection of traditional methods of woodland management as described earlier. These methods essentially involve rotational coppicing and skylighting, together with appropriate ride management to encourage the development of shrubby edges.

The management of woodlands for the holding and production of wild pheasants is of a form sympathetic to the conservation of many other species. The current pre-dominance of dark coniferous, or overgrown and unmanaged broadleaved woods has restricted the distributions of many of the species associated with light and open woodlands. Creating more diverse woodlands for pheasants should benefit many of these species and this is one of the side-benefits of game management that we shall examine in the next chapter.

PHEASANT MANAGEMENT IN THE UNITED STATES

In North America, pheasant shooting is much more dependent on the wild bird. As such they have diverted a great deal more attention to assessing the effects of agricultural intensification and developing methods of managing habitats than is the case in Britain. Their experiences with these techniques should be of especial relevance as agriculture in Britain is reformed and the scope for habitat management improves.

There are distinct similarities between the requirements of managed pheasants in North American and British populations, and yet there are major differences in the way in which they are harvested. Pheasants in the United States have suffered declines as a result of agricultural intensification. A large body of work has related declines in pheasants shot throughout the USA to an increase in the acreage of corn (maize) planted as a block monoculture on the native grassland plains. Burger (1987) described that following the introduction of the ring-necked pheasant in the late 1800s, principally in the western states, numbers increased, and during the 1930s pheasant hunting was at an all-time high. During this time about 80 million birds were harvested annually.

Game farm birds were hand-reared and released as a means of restocking and building up numbers to shoot. Following the Second World War however, farms moved from a traditional mixed system in which small grains (wheat, barley) and alfalfa were grown and livestock were pastured, to large areas of one or two crops, principally maize and soybeans. Ditches and fencelines were grubbed out, small woodlots were removed and the land ploughed and seeded with corn. Interestingly, even before the pheasant era early settlers believed that the prairie ecosystem was 'badland', unproductive and infertile, since no woodlands grew on them. Consequently they concentrated their farming effort on land they considered more likely to grow crops — that with well developed woodland and scrub. In removing much of this habitat they were destroying potential areas for pheasants in the years to come. The grassland prairies were held at their successional stage by North American Indians who burnt the land to encourage new vegetation growth and to herd buffalo during hunting.

After the 1930s and at the beginning of agricultural intensification, not only did pheasant densities decline (as indicated by harvest returns) but their distribution contracted, primarily to the Midwest states such as Minnesota, Michigan, Illinois, the Dakotas and Ohio. During the 1960s and 1970s numbers fell even further. In the Midwest in 1961, 12.5 million pheasants were harvested, compared to only 6.8 million in 1986 (Dahlgren 1987). Between 1971 and 1986 in North America as a whole, numbers declined from 19.6 million to 9.6 million. During the period 1961–1986 Midwest pheasant numbers harvested declined by a staggering 46%.

This decline has not only been restricted to pheasants. Indeed Brady (1987) reports a 90% decline in the abundance of most prairie grassland bird species since 1957, including larks, pipits and buntings.

Most releasing of hand-reared pheasants in North America was carried out between 1910 and 1940, but in the 1950s, faced with disappearing habitat, the practice declined in popularity. During the period 1940–1986, for example, the amount of nesting cover for pheasants has been estimated to have been reduced by about 50%. The government's approach during and immediately after the Second World War was that 'we can feed the world'. In attempting to fulfil this, the majority of permanent cover and old fencelines were removed, thereby depriving pheasants of places to nest. In some areas of the USA today one can view vistas of hundreds of square miles with maize being the only crop.

The method of hunting pheasants in the USA is very different from the large-scale driven shoots of the United Kingdom . In the USA the government plays a major role in organising and financially supporting research into game and wildlife habitat, through the US Fish and Wildlife Service, part of the Department of the Interior. Within each state there are Departments of Natural Resources or DNRs who devise and implement research and management work on game and wildlife. Throughout the USA, government sponsored release of hand-reared pheasants has now stopped, although as late as 1973 Michigan State still released birds for hunting. However, some small-scale releasing still goes on, paid for by private individuals. The birds are not released into open-topped pens as in Britain, but directly into crops, often as little as two hours before the hunt. Pheasants are not driven towards guns as in Britain but are hunted by perhaps a maximum of two people with dogs who walk slowly through an area. Bag limits are set on the number of birds which can be taken in the season, often restricted to two cocks at any one time. There are, however, a number of private shooting preserves such as the Max McGraw Wildlife Foundation near Chicago, and in the New England states, where pheasants are hunted in the same way as in any other part of the USA, although the licensee will ask for a certain number of birds and will pay for them before the hunt, usually equivalent to about 10 dollars per bird. On these private lands they are allowed to shoot both cocks and hens whereas on the majority of land owned by the state and by farmers, only cocks may be killed.

The continued interest in hunting by the majority of American people has caused governmental involvement in hunting at the highest level. State support for game and wildlife conservation is often more forthcoming than in Britain and this has led to the creation of special wildlife production areas and conservation reserve programmes. In these schemes farmers are compensated for leaving large areas uncropped, and they are seeded with native prairie grass species such as blue stem and switchgrass. Farmers annually receive approximately 50 dollars per acre for a period of 10 years (1987 values). After the 10-year period has expired farmers can once again profitably crop the land. During the conservation programme years, farmers may actually save money by spending less on machinery and maintenance, staff and pesticides.

In the prairie pothole regions these schemes are often developed alongside cattail management programmes. Cattail (*Typha* sp.) is a prolific bulrush which requires management if it is not to reduce the amounts of open water within potholes, which are also managed as waterfowl production areas. In states such as the Dakotas winter temperatures often fall below $-20°C$ and heavy blizzards can place severe physical stress on pheasants, as we discussed in Chapter 3. Cattails stand up well to such weather and offer vital shelter to these birds during winter months.

Technological advances in satellite imagery have enabled research biologists to map the location of pockets of suitable habitat which can be brought into the conservation reserve programme. Pattern recognition and habitat suitability indices are calculated for counties across all states, and areas which could benefit from the programme are visited and farmers encouraged to join the scheme. In those states which have little permanent cover, roadside management plans are devised whereby strips of habitat are left at the road edge. Such management, when compared to control areas with no management, has shown a doubling of pheasant numbers within a few years, due to greater nesting densities.

The conservation reserve programme views ideal pheasant habitat as consisting of 70–85% cropland, 10–25% grassland, and less than 10% forestland. However, it is agreed that the greatest limitation to distribution, in the face of good nesting and brood rearing cover, is caused by a lack of shrubby habitat which provides winter shelter.

This progressive approach to habitat management is being slightly hampered by the reluctance on the part of some farmers to join the scheme. The usual way pheasants are hunted is for the hunter to approach the farmer on whose land he wishes to shoot. This is the traditional way. In return for permission to hunt it is customary for the hunter to provide the farmer with a bird, together with a small token of thanks. However, some farmers believe that to encourage game on their land by inclusion in the conservation reserve programme will be to advertise that they have good hunting land, and will thus be inundated by requests for hunting, birdwatching etc. They feel that they can well do without such disturbance. The main point to note is that under the American constitution people have the right to bear arms and hunt over the land.

10   Bridging the Gap

From the point of view of the shooting community, pheasants represent the 'bread and butter' of fieldsports in Britain. As profit margins shrink on arable land, and as more emphasis is given to broadleaved trees by the Forestry Commission, the question we must ask is: How can pheasant management make a significant contribution to (a) land-use economics, and (b) the aesthetic fabric of the countryside?

The Nature Conservancy Council acknowledges in its publication *Nature Conservation in Great Britain* (1984) that 'the traditional land-owners' enthusiasm for fieldsports is closely linked to the conservation of habitat important to wildlife on farmland'. Large numbers of people including landowners and farmers hold game conservation close to their hearts. Each year since 1958 people have congregated at the annual Country Landowners' Association (CLA) Game Fair. This was initiated, in the words of the then president of the CLA, Sir John Ruggles-Brise, 'in order to attract keen shooting men and particularly farmers and small landowners to see something of modern methods of rearing and managing gamebirds in order to improve small shoots and to show how things can be fitted into good farming and forestry practice'. An initial hope of 2000 visitors was expected, but in the event 8500 were attracted. Today well in excess of 100 000 people visit the Game Fair. Therefore it can be seen that many people are motivated by field sports and there is great potential for encouraging sympathetic land management each year.

However, in spite of this, and the huge numbers of pheasants which are shot annually, we know little about the real value of shooting in conservation terms. How many, for example, carry out habitat management as an alternative or in addition to releasing hand-reared birds? Do estates which shoot pheasants indeed have significantly more woodland than those run by, for example, pension funds where emphasis is most likely to be on profit? What sacrifices are continually made on farms in favour of game management? Do pheasants really make a difference and can they make an even greater difference in the future? These are essential questions which must be answered if game management is to play a full role in the conservation of the countryside during the next few decades as the Common Agricultural Policy is reformed.

In this chapter we attempt to weigh the evidence by looking at the effects of habitat management for pheasants on other wildlife groups. We also attempt to place pheasant management into an economic framework and alongside this we discuss current thinking on achieving conservation objectives which involve management agreements, land purchase by conservation bodies and site designation. In many cases the value placed on pheasant management has made a difference to the rate of habitat loss since the end of the Second World War. For other habitats the role of pheasant management has been irrelevant. Nevertheless, as we showed in Chapter 9, habitats which are very important to the carrying capacity of pheasants, such as woodlands and hedgerows, have been lost at an alarming rate. Farming practices have also changed so much that they are now often hostile environments to gamebird chicks.

A SURVEY OF LANDOWNERS

In 1983 the Standing Conference on Countryside Sports published a report detailing results of a survey of landowner attitudes to their landscape carried out by Cobham Resource Consultants (1983). The purpose was to investigate the contribution made by the various countryside sports to the national economy of Great Britain. As Lord Porchester stated: 'I sincerely hope that the results of this independent survey will lead to a better understanding of countryside sports by those who, up to now, may not have appreciated their impact on the national economy, their contribution to the landscape and to quality of life in the countryside.'

At 1982 prices, the survey calculated that direct expenditure on shooting (which will largely be pheasant shooting) was £212 m. Employment generated as a result of shooting amounted to some 12 200 jobs which included over 4000 full-time gamekeepers and 700 stalkers. The value of the game shot, which again was largely pheasants, was £17.4 m. Over 90% of pheasants sold in Britain are exported with a visible export value of just under £5.8 m (Overseas Trade Statistics HM Customs & Excise, 1980).

Both Central and Local Government derive income from shooting. There are rates levied by local authorities on the owners of sporting rights in England and Wales, and the occupier in Scotland. Payment for licences and certificates bring the treasury another sum. Value Added Tax is also collected on sporting equipment, National Health Insurance contributions and taxes as a result of employment of staff to run the shoot, such as gamekeepers. Income to Government from shooting amounts to some £20 m. Income tax and National Health Insurance amount to another £5 m.

The survey was also able to conclude that countryside sports were the fourth most popular form of recreational pursuit including, in descending order of importance, walking, football and running. More time was spent by the population in country sports than in golfing, camping, cycling or playing tennis.

But what opinions did those landowners surveyed have on the

objectives of conservation and the creation of countryside features? The survey looked at two very important aspects. First, the reasons given by the sample of occupiers throughout Great Britain for both retaining and planting small woods. Second, the level of expenditure incurred by the organisers of shoots on the provision and improvement of sporting habitats in the previous five years. Figure 10.1 shows that 67% of respondents claimed that game interests were a reason for retaining existing woodland features, and 56% said that game was also a reason for planting new woods. Game was second only to maintaining beauty in the landscape as a reason for conservation measures on respondents' estates. By comparison, wildlife conservation was ranked fifth and sixth respectively for planting or retaining existing woodland. It would appear from these statistics that landowners view direct benefits from game higher than they do pure conservation interests. In terms of effecting change in the way land is managed, persuasion, with game as the supporting argument, is more likely to lead to success than pure conservation incentives.

THE POPULAR CONSERVATION MOVEMENT

Wildlife conservation has gained immense popularity during the past 20 years and concerns for our well-being and what we do with our environment have been taken into the political arena. Nowadays political parties justifiably concentrate a good deal of time in presenting their views on conservation and environmental issues, although many consider that much more emphasis should be given to the cause.

There are presently almost 50 national voluntary groups concerned with rural and nature conservation. Many are small groups with limited influence, whilst the two largest, the National Trust and the Royal Society for the Protection of Birds (RSPB), carry considerable political clout. The RSPB manage 121 reserves covering an area of almost 70 000 ha in 1987. Save for the Audubon Society in the United States, the RSPB is the largest voluntary conservation body of its kind in the world, with nearly 600 000 members.

The Royal Society for Nature Conservation is the national co-ordinating body for the 46 county trusts for nature conservation which give advice to farmers, landowners and local authorities.

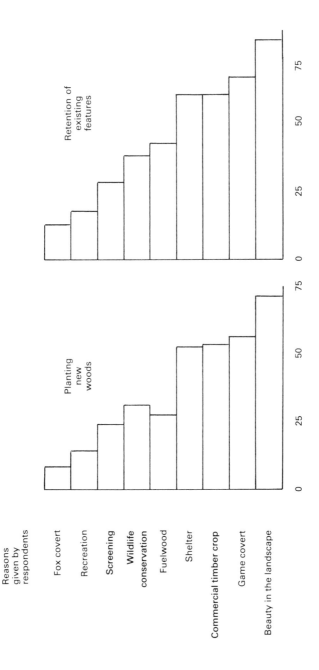

Fig. 10.1 Results of a survey of landowners on the reasons for retaining woodlands or planting new ones. (Redrawn from Cobham 1983.)

The Council for the Protection of Rural England (with Scottish and Welsh equivalents) and the Ramblers' Association are particularly concerned with landscape and amenity protection. These voluntary groups all have a vested interest in land-use and often raise questions in the Houses of Parliament regarding areas of land-use conflict. The sheer weight of numbers of people who are actively interested in the countryside represent a formidable observer of land-use practices.

Interest in countryside affairs is growing and it is imperative that recreational land-uses, such as pheasant management, be explained and discussed by all concerned.

A further important change in the past decade has been the increase in the coverage of wildlife programmes on television. For example, some 9 million people regularly watch 'Wildlife on One'. As Lowe et al. (1986) state, 'television has been responsible for establishing nature as a central feature of popular culture'. A public opinion survey conducted by MORI in 1982 showed that 53% of 1991 respondents said they would support an increase in income tax of one penny in the pound to pay for measures to protect wildlife and the environment, compared to 26% who said they would oppose such a move. Thirty-one per cent said that they had donated money to a charity concerned with conservation within the last year, and 4% of respondents said they belonged to a conservation organisation. As the general public's awareness of countryside issues is increased in this way, so their demand to influence change will also rise. This is one of the strongest reasons why the shooting fraternity should take stock of its conservation position, publicise its successes and learn from its failures.

THE ECONOMICS OF WOODLAND MANAGEMENT FOR PHEASANTS

A number of recent publications have espoused the benefit which pheasant shooting makes to the fabric of the countryside (Shoard 1980, Lowe et al. 1986), and yet an attempt at quantification of this has never been made. Undoubtedly pheasant shooting contributes to the rural economy as we have described, and provides employment for many of the 4000 full-time keepers. The subsidiary 'industries' such as gunmakers, game-feed specialists, sporting magazines, etc., all exist mainly because of pheasant shooting interests. But to place a figure in monetary terms is, as we have seen, rather difficult. However, it is possible to make some rule-of-thumb comparisons of the contributions of timber production and sporting revenue to small woodland economics. This is a large and complex topic. The sporting revenue generated by an area is affected by a large number of factors including topography, proximity to large towns and climate as well as the actual density of birds on the estate. This discussion simply aims to illustrate the potential value, using average figures, of the sporting revenue to be generated by a 160 ha estate in Hampshire.

This hypothetical estate is assumed to have been planned with shooting in mind. The estate includes 20% of woodland in 16 blocks of 2 ha, sufficient to provide two separate shoots of eight drives per day.

To a large extent the value of the shooting rights is determined by the quality and arrangement of the woodlands. However the revenue generated in this way is paid over the whole land area of the estate. Thus if the woods in question were well laid out it is quite possible for the sporting rent to amount to £12.50 per ha over the entire 160 ha, or £2000 per year.

If these woods were beech that had been planted in a manner unsympathetic to game, the sporting revenue could be negligible. The bare ground layer typical of mature beech stands is unsuitable as holding cover for pheasants. However it would only require suitable siting for sport and slight sacrifices of forestry practice, most noticeably the inclusion of rides, provision of a shrub layer and planting some form of shrubby edge, to raise the value of these woods to the levels mentioned above.

Assuming a rotation of 120 years for beech it can be seen that the sporting revenue generated by sympathetic planting over this period could amount to £240 000 or £7500 per ha of woodland at present day prices and without compound interest. This is rather higher than the £2500 to £6500 per ha value of most standing beech and is of course in addition to the value of the timber.

Although including consideration beneficial for gamebirds in woodland planting may require a compromise with the aims of pure timber production, it can be seen that it can provide a substantial asset and improve the value of the wood. One of the major considerations may be the size of woodland blocks; smaller blocks tend to have a higher edge to area ratio than larger stands and as such are more attractive to pheasants. Furthermore, many of the existing small woodlands on farmland are of this small size and the management of these could be highly beneficial for pheasants.

In addition to the benefits to be obtained through increased sporting revenue, the government has significantly increased the subsidies available for woodland planting. The Forestry Commission's Woodland Grant Scheme has been aimed at increasing the planting of hardwoods while the Farm Woodlands Scheme has the aim of encouraging landowners to take land out of agricultural production. While both of these schemes provide monetary incentives to encourage planting, their stipulations as regards the inclusion of non-timber species such as berry trees and shrubs and the provisions for rides and edge management make them of limited use when designing a game covert. The shortcomings will decrease attractiveness of the schemes to many landowners, lower the value of the resulting woods and seriously detract from the many potential benefits to conservation.

WOODLAND CONSERVATION

The Nature Conservancy Council have described 63 woodland stand types based on species composition, geographical variation and soil conditions, which aggregate into 12 broad categories (Peterken 1981). These refer to ancient semi-natural woodland. Whilst many woodlands used for pheasant shooting are ancient semi-natural, many others have a more recent history and are therefore rated less valuable in conservation terms.

However, there are a number of underlying principles which we can apply to woods which are designed for pheasants in order to show how these designs may affect the other species that use them. Any woodland can be extremely complex in terms of physical factors such as horizontal and vertical structure, light penetration, or the species of wildlife associated with it.

Initially we shall discuss the impact of pheasant management on other birds. The first feature of a woodland considered relates to the tree species composition. Oak is the most widespread type of woodland in Britain and has a greater number of invertebrates associated with it than any other tree, apart from some species of willow. Most birds show a low degree of tree specialisation compared with invertebrates, and it is generally accepted that for birds the woodland structure is more important (Fuller 1982),

although there are exceptions. There are of course broad areas of
selection, for example some species are usually found in deciduous
and not coniferous woodland, whilst for other species the reverse
is true. Usually density and species richness are higher in broadleaved than in coniferous woods, although in many cases woods
containing a mixture of conifer and broadleaf hold higher overall
densities of birds but not necessarily a greater diversity than each
stand type on its own. Stands containing a dominance of certain
species such as oak or birch usually have higher densities and
diversity than stands containing other species such as sweet chestnut. It is probable that tree species influence bird density and
communities by affecting food supply. Non-native trees are believed to hold fewer species and numbers of invertebrates. Consequently, there are fewer upon which birds can feed, particularly
during the summer chick rearing period. In winter too, an absence
of fruit-bearing shrubs, particularly at the edge of woods, will
mean an impoverished bird fauna. Many species of bird show
high adaptation for feeding within a relatively narrow food niche
either in terms of species of food eaten or in terms of the physical
position in which it searches for food. For example, the six species
of tits living in England occupy different feeding positions within
the woodland. Other species occupy a narrow breeding site niche
such as holes in dead trees. In general, tree species composition
has little direct effect on pheasant density although mixed broadleaf and coniferous woods can offer better structure and more
feeding niches. There should therefore be no conflict between
pheasant management and broader conservation aims when considering tree species alone.

The second important physical feature is woodland structure.
We have described, in a previous chapter, our definition of vertical structure based on different height categories such as ground
layer, herb layers, shrub layer, and canopy. In some woods these
layers are continuous and no obvious structure is apparent.
Horizontal structure such as that provided by rides, edges, variation in stocking density, and open spaces, is also very important.

Soil conditions, age of woodland, exposure and silvicultural
history all combine to alter woodland structure. In conservation
terms, many southern lowland woods are of conservation interest
because of their diverse structure which provides habitat to a
wide diversity of bird species. Pheasants select areas with a high
diversity of both vertical and horizontal structure, and such diverse
structures are often the aim of managers when improving the

conservation value of a wood. Woods on less productive soils such as the western sessile oak woods are less diverse in structure usually because of heavy grazing pressure, but are important habitats for other species such as redstart, pied flycatcher, tree pipit and wood warbler. Although areas such as these should be conserved in their existing form, most other woods will benefit from the increased structural diversity resulting from being managed for pheasants.

Structure is the most important component of a woodland to pheasants. Patchiness within the woodland, giving rise to horizontal structural diversity, also appears important, with clearings being of high value. If we look at the optimum habitat requirements of 25 widely distributed woodland species we can see that the thicket stage of development is used by a wide diversity of birds but is important to only a few, although the value of over-mature woods with plenty of dead wood is also evident (Table 10.1). Pheasants find optimal habitat at the pre-thicket and thicket stage as do certain warbler species such as garden warbler and nightingale. Shrubby cover between 1 and 2 metres is also important for many other songbirds. Ford (1987) found that woods with a well developed shrub layer at this height contained higher densities of songbirds.

Coppicing may not be ideal for creating a rich diversity of bird species. However, it is of vital importance to the maintenance of high density in many ground species of plants, and the animals which feed on them. The regular cutting of each area within a wood periodically provides the light conditions in which the accumulated seed bank can germinate. Woods which have been coppiced in rotation for many years erupt in a glory of wild flowers when cut. Similarly, these areas provide rich nectar sources and a multitude of host plants for insects.

However, active coppicing has declined dramatically throughout this century and it could be said that our woods are now shadier than at any time in the last thousand years (Thomas and Webb 1984). As a direct consequence, many species once associated with light open woodlands have declined, often to calamitous levels. These include many species of butterfly such as chequered skippers, pearl bordered, lesser pearl bordered, high brown, heath and Duke of Burgundy fritillaries.

We have already described the value of coppice rotations to pheasants and in many areas we believe the resurrection of coppice and the conversion of derelict coppice woodland back to an

Table 10.1 Habitat requirements of some widely distributed birds associated with broadleaved woodlands (From Andrews and Smart 1985)

KEY
○ Feeding   ● Optimal
− Nesting   ● Suitable
= Perching   • Marginal
≡ Nesting and Perching

Species	Favoured stage of the forestry cycle					Important features required						
	clear fell	pre-thicket	thicket	high forest	over-mature	bare soil	litter layer	ground/field layers	shrub layer	tree canopy	trunks/branches	snags/dead trees
Coal tit				●	●		○	○	○	○	−	−
Lesser spotted woodpecker				●	●					○	○/=	○/=
Pied flycatcher			•	●	●		○	○	○			○/≡
Wood warbler			•	●	●		−	○	○			
Green woodpecker			•	●	●	○	○	○			○/=	○/=
Great spotted woodpecker			•	●	●					○	○/=	○/=
Marsh tit			•	●	●		○	○	○			−
Nuthatch			•	●	●					○	○/=	○/=
Redstart			•	●	●		○	○			−	−
Tawny owl			•	●	●	○	○	○			≡	−
Jay			●	●	●		○		○/=	○		
Treecreeper		•	●	●	●				○	○	○/=	−
Sparrowhawk			●	●	●		○	○			−	≡
Woodcock	•	●	●	●	●	○	○/=	○				
Hawfinch			●	●	●		○	○	○/=	○/=	=	=
Spotted flycatcher			•	●	●					○	=	≡
Chiffchaff			•	●	●		−		○	○/=		
Blackcap		•	●	●	●		○	○/=	○			
Turtle dove			●	●	●	○		○	−			
Wren	●	●	●	●	●		−	○	○/=			
Garden warbler		●	●	●				○	○/=	○		
Long-tailed tit		●	●	●					○/=	○		
Nightingale		●	●	•					○/=			
Tree pipit	●	●			●		○	○/=		≡	=	=
Nightjar	●	●					−	−				=

actively managed situation could be achieved by emphasising the benefits accrued to game. In conservation terms coppicing or the diversification of the shrub layer will provide better habitats for many other animals. However, for high forest species such as woodpeckers, pied flycatchers and redstarts, conversion to a short coppice cycle would be detrimental. However, high forest is not currently in short supply, as opposed to actively managed coppice. Nevertheless, a mosaic of different ages of coppice adjacent to larger areas of high forest is likely to offer the best compromise for game and wildlife interests.

Plate XVI. The creation of light, open woodlands to encourage shrubs for pheasants also benefits a host of other plant species, such as primrose. (*P.A. Robertson*).

The third important physical feature of a woodland is its size and shape. We have shown that woods larger than 1–2 ha are used less by pheasants, and woods with scalloped edges which offer a higher edge to volume ratio are better because of the greater shelter and feeding areas they provide. Classic theories of 'island biogeography' have shown that small islands have fewer species of birds and other taxa than larger ones, and that the more isolated an island the fewer species it will hold. Islands need not be surrounded by water; an ecological analogy is a woodland surrounded by fields. This certainly seems to be important for those species with limited powers of dispersal such as wild flowers and certain butterflies. In some cases these may need to be helped to recolonise woods where they have been lost in order to speed up their recovery. Other, more mobile groups such as birds may not encounter such problems. One study which looked at the density of songbirds in woods of different sizes found that small woods contained significantly higher densities than larger ones. While woods of 0.5 ha contained an average of 35 birds per ha, this fell to around 10 per ha in woods of 5–10 ha (Ford 1987). Small woods are also the best for pheasants as we described in

Chapter 3, in fact the relationships between both pheasant density and songbird density in relation to woodland area are almost identical. The promotion of small woodlands for pheasant shooting should have direct benefits for many other species of woodland bird.

The fourth physical feature of importance is the productivity of the land. Certain woods in Kent with gravel overlying clay, and some upland woods, have trees which exhibit much slower patterns of growth. Coppicing in these woods (apart from sweet chestnut) is considered unproductive and even after the canopy is opened up little ground flora and shrubby cover develops. Under these circumstances such woods are often poor habitats for pheasants and also exhibit an impoverished bird fauna.

Finally, the patterns of management, both current and historical, can affect the value of woodlands to conservation. Older woods tend to contain the richest flora and fauna, although the types of management are of utmost importance. For instance, old high forest or long-term coppice can both constitute ancient woodland yet contain radically different populations.

On our study area at Wimborne St Giles in Dorset we were interested to measure the relationship between the use made by pheasants and other bird species of a series of small plots in order to document the value or otherwise of managing habitats for pheasants. Many of the areas were managed by retaining the shrub layer through thinning and the creation of rides. We located 32 points within the mosaic of woodland types and ages and counted all pheasant droppings within a 20 m $\times$ 10 m grid at each point. Pheasant droppings provide a measure of pheasant activity in the area. We then carried out three early morning point counts of birds and took the maximum figures for numbers of individuals and species counted at each point. We found a close correlation between the index of pheasant abundance (determined by faecal counts), and both the number of species of other birds ($r=0.70$, $P<0.001$) and the number of individuals ($r=0.69$, $P<0.001$) (Figs 10.2 and 10.3). Those areas most attractive to pheasants also appear to contain the highest numbers of species and individuals of other bird species. We should point out that diversity in the formal sense of the word is only one criterion on which the Nature Conservancy Council judge the conservation quality of a site.

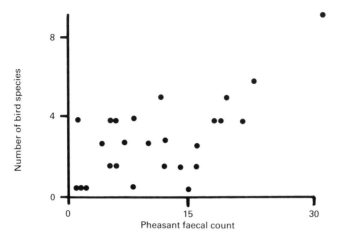

Fig. 10.2 Relationship between the number of pheasant faeces counted on a 20 m × 10 m grid and number of bird species counted using point counting techniques standing at the grid centre, for 32 grid points on an estate at Wimborne St Giles, Dorset.

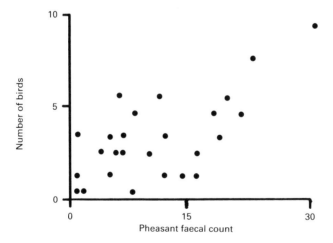

Fig. 10.3 Relationship between the number of pheasant faeces counted on a 20 m × 10 m grid and number of individual birds counted using point counting techniques standing at the grid centre, for 32 grid points on an estate at Wimborne St Giles, Dorset.

The impact of modern forestry practice by converting broad-leaved woodland to conifers has been deleterious for most woodland species of wild flowers, birds and butterflies, although it has benefited a few. In general, most groups only benefit from coniferisation during the early establishment phase of the operation in much the same way as it benefits pheasants. Once the trees shade out the ground and shrub flora, species abundance and richness decline. Small areas of conifers within broadleaved stands do not encounter these problems and can increase the cover available within a wood. For this reason, they are often incorporated into the planting of woods for pheasants. Conifers are also used as nurse crops during the establishment of new broad-leaved plantations, and these can be removed and sold after the broadleaves have established. It may even be possible to sell some species either as Christmas trees or fence posts.

Woodland rides are another important feature of both pheasant coverts and commercial woodland. They are also important in conservation terms. However, the quality of rides varies immensely from one woodland to another. In many of the derelict hazel coppice woodlands in the south, where rides were once used for extracting coppice products, they are now almost completely grown over. In some commercial forestry plantations, on the other hand, the ride may be very large in order to facilitate the extraction of large timber but in lacking diversity of shrub species it offers little as a wildlife habitat. Indeed, the Forestry Commission now have a policy of planting up some wide rides with a variety of native shrubs and broadleaved trees as part of their campaign towards greater conservation awareness. In spite of their obvious importance both economically and commercially woodland rides have, until recently, received little research attention.

The game manager needs rides for a number of reasons: they attract pheasants into large woods by providing extra 'edges', and provide flushing points and positions for the guns on shooting days. Furthermore, they provide sites for winter feeding, extra areas for breeding birds and sites for deer control. The commercial timber grower on the other hand requires rides in order to inspect growing trees, extract thinnings or larger timber trees and to act as firebreakers.

To the conservationist, rides serve a number of useful functions and are of value for a variety of reasons. They may be examples of unimproved grassland because of their lack of interference or, if properly managed, resemble the rich flora of newly cut coppice. Many rides on wet soils have a rich marsh community of plants. Open rides which receive plenty of light are the best types for invertebrates whereas shaded rides often have a ground flora which more closely resembles that of derelict coppice or high forest rather than unshaded grassland. The ecotone created between the ride margin and the woodland is generally the most important component of the ride. Irregular and diffuse rather than sharp and hard edges are best, in which the track merges through tall herbs and shrubs into the woodland canopy.

So what type of ride is best for pheasants, and is this useful to other species of wildlife? In a small covert, a central ride of 20 m width is often used and the central 8 m portion of this is left to grass. Shrubs such as spindle, hawthorn, hazel, and blackthorn are encouraged and managed so as to create a gradual slope to the canopy trees. The rides are ideally maintained by mowing the grass once or twice a year with an infrequently cut marginal strip of 3 m on each side of the ride. Sometimes the edge strip is colonised with bramble which is a useful species to encourage so long as it does not become dominant. Rides are often scalloped and widened irregularly down their length. This has two functions: first, it creates potentially more edge for territorial male pheasants, and second, it acts as a wind baffle, effectively making the ride 'warmer'.

In order to assess the use made of rides created for pheasants by another group, we monitored butterfly densities on the Wimborne St Giles estate (Robertson, Woodburn and Hill in press). Counts of butterflies were made on a series of twenty-six 200 m transects using the methods described by Pollard (1977) and Hall (1981). These counts were conducted at ten-day intervals during July and August 1986. The transects covered a variety of different habitat types including coniferous plantations, areas of unmanaged broadleaves, similar areas thinned and skylighted for the benefit of pheasants, large rides cut through the woods to provide stands for the guns and woodland edges. A total of 842 butterflies of 21 different species were seen during the study period. Significantly more were seen in those areas of woodland that had been managed for pheasants (an average of 46.7 per km) compared to coniferous or broadleaved areas which had not been managed (an average of 3.5 per km). The numbers of each species seen in each habitat type and the corresponding numbers per km are presented in Table 10.2. The pheasant rides contained the highest numbers of 17 of the 21 species seen. These rides also contained the highest number of species of any of the habitat types under consideration.

The rides created specifically for pheasant shooting on this estate contained significantly more butterflies than did woodland edges, which are the nearest equivalent habitat type found in unmanaged woodland. Of the 11 species seen in sufficient numbers for statistical analysis, 8 were significantly more abundant on pheasant rides (Table 10.3).

We also found that woodlands with an open canopy, created to encourage pheasants, contained more individuals than closed canopy plantations and derelict areas, hardly surprising since butterflies need sunny areas in which to fly and remain active. Also, 7 of the 8 species compared proved to be at higher density in the open woodland than in closed canopy areas (Table 10.4).

Consequently we concluded that woodland management intended to benefit pheasants in winter can also provide better habitats for many woodland butterflies during the summer. The simplest method of improving an area of unmanaged woodland for pheasants is to remove 5–10% of the standards to increase the penetration of light to the woodland floor. The resultant increase in shrubby plants provides good shelter for pheasants in winter and food plants and an open canopy for butterflies in summer.

The provision of habitats for butterflies within woodland is seen as a major conservation objective largely because of the decline in traditional woodcraft which maintained many woods in states suitable for these insects. Only 2% of the woodlands in Dorset, for example, still provide the sunny open conditions that are essential for most of the traditional species of woodland butter-flies, the remainder being increasingly shady as described earlier (Hill and Edwards 1986). Many species of butterfly associated with such open woodland have declined during the latter half of this century while those more tolerant of shade, such as the white

Table 10.2 The numbers of butterflies per km on transects in five woodland types on a pheasant shooting estate in Dorset, July and August 1986

Species	Pheasant ride		Open wood		Woodland edge		Conifer plant'n		Broadleaf plant'n	
	n	n/km	n	n/km	n	n/km	n	n/km	n	n/km
Large white	22	4.6	4	0.4	1	0.2	–	–	–	–
Small white	52	10.8	16	1.7	12	2.5	–	–	1	0.1
Green-veined white	–		2	0.2	–		–	–	–	–
Marbled white	7	1.4	35	3.6	2	0.4	–	–	–	–
Brimstone	7	1.4	2	0.2	–		–	–	–	–
Speckled wood	15	3.1	15	1.6	4	0.8	23	4.8	8	1.1
Meadow brown	76	15.8	36	3.7	72	5.0	–	–	6	0.8
Wall	3	0.6	1	0.1	–		–	–	–	–
Hedge brown	33	6.9	13	1.3	4	0.8	–	–	–	–
Ringlet	39	8.1	74	7.7	25	5.2	–	–	–	–
Painted lady	–		1	0.1	–		–	–	–	–
Peacock	3	0.6	–		1	0.2	–	–	–	–
Comma	2	0.4	–		–		–	–	–	–
Small tortoiseshell	1	0.2	–		–		–	–	–	–
White admiral	14	2.9	1	0.1	–		2	0.4	–	–
Pearl bordered fritillary	2	0.4	1	0.1	1	0.2	–	–	2	0.3
Silver washed fritillary	30	6.2	15	1.6	2	0.4	–	–	–	–
Large skipper	18	3.7	27	2.8	5	1.0	–	–	–	–
Small skipper	3	0.6	1	0.1	–		–	–	–	–
Common blue	1	0.2	–		–		–	–	–	–
Small copper	1	0.2	–		–		–	–	–	–
Total	429		244		129		25		17	
No. species	19		16		11		2		4	
No. km sampled	4.8		9.6		4.8		4.8		7.2	
No. per km	89.4		25.4		26.9		5.2		2.4	

Table 10.3 Comparison of butterfly numbers on pheasant rides and woodland edges on a pheasant shooting estate in Dorset 1986

Species	Pheasant ride	Woodland edge	Significant difference
Large white	22	1	***
Small white	52	12	***
Marbled white	7	2	ns
Brimstone	7	0	**
Speckled wood	15	4	*
Meadow brown	76	72	ns
Hedge brown	33	4	***
Ringlet	39	25	ns
White admiral	14	0	***
Silver washed fritillary	30	2	***
Large skipper	18	5	**
Total	429	129	***
No. km sampled	4.8	4.8	

*** $P < 0.001$
** $P < 0.01$
* $P < 0.05$
ns not statistically significant

Table 10.4 Comparison of the butterflies observed in open woodland or in plantations and derelict woodland on a pheasant shooting estate in Dorset 1986

Species	Open wood	Plantation or unmanaged broadleaf	Significant difference
Small white	16	1	***
Marbled white	35	0	***
Speckled wood	15	31	ns
Meadow brown	36	6	***
Hedge brown	13	0	***
Ringlet	74	0	***
Silver washed fritillary	15	2	***
Large skipper	27	0	***
Total	244	42	***
No. km sampled	9.6	12.0	

*** $P < 0.001$
ns not statistically significant

admiral and speckled wood, have increased. The recent spread of the few species that require more shady conditions reinforces the belief that it is alterations to woodland structure that have been of paramount importance in determining changes in the status of these butterflies.

An initial study of the effects of a number of different types of woodland management for pheasants on the ground flora was also carried out on the Wimborne St Giles estate (Bealey and Ludolf 1988, Ludolf, Robertson and Woodburn in press). The area of woodland under study was thought to be ancient in character, i.e. it has been under almost continuous tree cover since AD 1600.

The past management of the woodland was categorised into six distinct types, ranging from young coppice to mature conifer plantation (Table 10.5). Of these habitat types, the rides and young coppice were both managed specifically for pheasants. In each type, the total number of field and herb layer species, the number of Ancient Woodland Indicator Species (those species identified by the Nature Conservancy Council as being locally characteristic of ancient, semi-natural woodland), and their estimated percentage cover, were recorded in a series of 25 0.5 m ^{2} quadrants arranged at 5 m intervals on a 25 m × 25 m grid.

Table 10.5 Sample sites for the plant surveys situated on the Wimborne St Giles Estate in East Dorset

Management category	Description
Unmanaged coppice	Hazel coppice with between 17 and 30 years regrowth under oak
Managed coppice	Hazel coppice with between 1 and 3 years regrowth under oak
High forest	Mixed mature trees (mainly oak and ash), heavy canopy, no understorey
Ride	10 to 15 year old rides, 25 to 50 m in width, cut annually
Young conifer	4 to 10 year old plantations, open canopy, mainly Norway spruce and Douglas fir
Mature conifer	Plantations of mainly Douglas fir, Scots pine and larch, closed canopy

Results were recorded for both the spring and summer periods.

The only major difference between the two sampling periods was in percentage cover. As expected, greater cover was recorded in the summer, particularly in the high forest and rides where bracken had become a dominant species.

Figure 10.4 shows the mean total number of species and the mean number of Ancient Woodland Indicator species found in each management category over both sampling periods. These included species such as the conspicuous wood anemone (*Anemone nemorosa*) and the inobtrusive moschatel (*Adoxa moschatellina*). There was a significant difference among the six types (ANOVA,

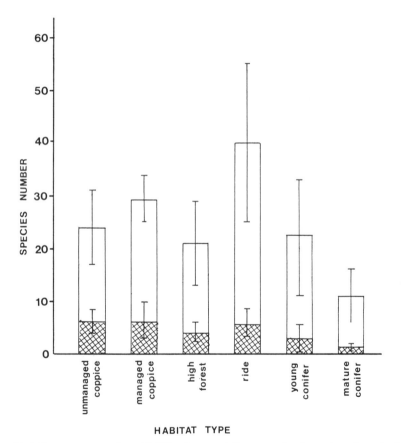

Fig. 10.4 The mean number (±SE) of ground flora species (open) and ancient woodland indicator species (hatched) recorded in each management category on Wimborne St Giles. The managed coppice and ride were habitats specifically managed for pheasants. (Ludolf Robertson and Woodburn in press.)

$F=3.94$; $P<0.01$). The only outstanding results were the much greater number of species in rides, and the somewhat less outstanding increase in number of species in managed coppice. There was also a very much lower number of species in mature conifer. In fact, mature conifer had only 27% of the total number of species found in rides.

An interesting aspect of the data was the lack of similarity between the coppice (both types) and the mature conifer and rides as measured by the presence of Ancient Woodland Indicator Species. The lack of similarity with mature conifer was not surprising and provides good evidence of the detrimental effect of shade and increased soil acidity on ancient woodland ground flora. The lack of similarity with rides was, however, almost certainly due to the management regimes which tend to favour a large number of short-lived marginal species such as the foxglove (*Digitalis purpurea*) and ruderal (waste ground type) species such as rose bay willowherb (*Chamaenerion angustifolium*) in the rides.

An index of diversity (a statistic which combines the species richness and abundance of cover in an area) was calculated for all sites. Again rides and managed coppice came out with the overall highest scores over both sampling periods, although the old coppice also had a fairly high score. Overall differences among the types were significant for both the spring period ($F=3.63$; $P<0.02$) and summer period ($F=2.66$; $P<0.05$).

So what do these results mean and how do they relate to woodland management for game and its effects on wildlife? The managed coppice (by small coupes) and rides were managed very much with pheasant in mind and it is perhaps a comparison between these and the other four categories that should be made when evaluating the effects on the flora. In this respect, active management for pheasants does come out favourably, and appears to increase or at least maintain both the number of flowering plants (including Ancient Woodland Indicator Species) and overall plant species diversity. Beyond the effects on the management of existing woods, the role of pheasant shooting in maintaining these woods and creating new ones should not be forgotten.

In general, woodland management for pheasants aims to create a diversity of structure that is all too often lacking in the dark and uniform structure of many woods today. This variety in turn benefits a wide range of other species, the welfare of birds, butterflies and wild flowers all providing good indicators of the wider conservation interest in the area. Pheasant management is one of the few factors giving an economic incentive for active management and diversity in our woodlands. While conservation bodies can protect small areas of especial interest, game interests have a wide effect on the management of the countryside as a whole.

CONSERVATION IN CEREAL FIELDS

Cereal fields provide the most common habitats for rearing pheasant broods in lowland Britain. Although uncultivated weedy areas and certain other crops may provide better conditions for chicks, cereals are used the most. As we have described, increased pesticide use on these crops has caused declines in the numbers of insects on which young gamebird chicks feed and this has been implicated as one reason for the decline of the grey partridge (Potts 1980, 1986). Although pheasant populations do not appear to have suffered to the same degree, partly due to the effects of hand rearing, improving chick survival should provide an increased wild bird component to the bag.

Gamebirds are not the only species to have suffered from the increasing sterility of our cereal fields. The Botanical Society of the British Isles (BSBI) lists 25 species of arable weeds which are now considered uncommon or rare, including species such as corn-chamomile which were a common sight not many years ago (Wilson 1987). The absence of such flowering plants as a result of weed control may have made nectar a scarce resource and many of our butterflies and other nectar feeding insects such as bumble-bees may have suffered as a result.

Intensively farmed land has, until recently, received relatively little attention from conservationists. Following its work in Sussex the Game Conservancy established the Cereals and Gamebirds Research Project in 1983 to examine the effects of modern farming practices on gamebirds and other flora and fauna which traditionally shared the farming environment. The aim was to provide practical management plans for the conservation of gamebirds and other wildlife on arable farms while not significantly compromising general standards of cereal production or jeopardising farming profits.

Much of this work has concentrated on modifying pesticide applications to crop margins, incorporating 6 m strips around the perimeter of cereal fields. These are the areas used most by gamebird chicks and often produce the lowest crop yields. They are often overshadowed by woods or hedges which further reduce yield and increase moisture content of the crop. Carefully modifying pesticide use on these areas can increase the numbers of certain broadleaved weeds and associated insect fauna without causing excessive reductions in crop yields. By adopting the use of these 'conservation' headlands it has been possible to almost double the survival of gamebird chicks, both grey partridge and pheasant, compared to normally sprayed areas (Potts 1986). Other forms of farmland wildlife have also benefited. Many more butterflies are observed on selectively sprayed headlands compared to their fully sprayed counterparts (Table 10.6) (Sotherton *et al.* in press). This appears to be due to their providing extra sources of nectar, an otherwise limited resource in the arable environment.

Table 10.6 The numbers of different butterflies seen in sprayed and 'conservation' headlands, north-east Hampshire, 1984, 1985. Taken from Sotherton, Dover and Rands (in press)

	1984 'Conservation'	Sprayed	1985 'Conservation'	Sprayed
Brimstone	52	10	17	5
Common blue	18	1	0	0
Green-veined white	140	21	196	176
Gatekeeper	93	59	134	32
Holly blue	29	13	3	2
Large skipper	17	1	10	4
Large white	56	38	13	20
Meadow brown	123	46	109	32
Orange tip	11	0	1	1
Peacock	39	19	29	2
Ringlet	52	23	17	6
Small heath	11	0	0	0
Small skipper	41	2	6	1
Small tortoiseshell	95	42	131	77
Small white	19	14	1	3
Speckled wood	10	2	3	0
Wall	9	4	0	0
Transect length (km)	3.6	3.2	2.1	2.3
Total	815	295	670	373

This has important effects on the holding capacity of the area for butterflies and their subsequent exploitation of adjacent host plants on non-cropped areas.

A survey of rare arable weeds (Wilson 1986, 1987) has also demonstrated the benefits of conservation headlands. A survey of the headlands of 17 farms where these practices were in use found a considerable number of interesting and scarce species, including 18 of the 25 listed by the BSBI.

The agronomic costs of such headlands remain to be accurately defined. However, a rough assessment suggests that they may only reduce the total yield of the average field by less than 0.5% (Boatman 1987). Despite the small scale of these losses it is unlikely that many landowners would be willing to accept them were it not for the benefits to game. It is the ability of game management to gain the ear of landowners and to make them compromise intensive farming practices that allows scope for the conservation of other wildlife on many of our farms.

WINTER FEEDING

We mentioned in the last section that one reason for planting and managing woodland rides was to provide open areas where pheasants can be fed during the winter. Such feeding places need to be well sheltered. This is achieved by a shrubby edge to the ride on each side, together with the type of scalloped design which reduces wind. The grain or sometimes specialist game-feed which is fed to pheasants on such rides is also eaten by winter flocks of finches including chaffinch, brambling, yellowhammer, greenfinch, and sometimes siskin and redpoll. Jays also feed at pheasant feeding sites as do many species of small mammals and some deer. It is common to see squirrels feeding at grain hoppers and these can be a serious problem in a woodland where food is provided for pheasants. Certain species such as beech and sycamore are particularly vulnerable to squirrel damage. It is probably true that woods where pheasants are fed contain higher densities of squirrels as a result of the extra food provided. This may seem to be detrimental to timber production, but as these pheasant feeding sites are predictably used by squirrels from a large area, they may provide ideal opportunities for cost-effective control.

This may more than account for any temporary increase in squirrel density.

No study has yet been conducted on the use made by other species of pheasant feeding hoppers and grain spread by hand. It is possible that where much food is liberally spread this could make a significant contribution to weight maintenance of small birds, particularly during the hardest weather.

CONSERVATION CONFLICTS

There are a number of activities carried out by the shoot in the name of pheasant management which are an anathema to the conservationist, and we must take the opportunity of outlining them here. A number of problems arise over the following:

(1) The use of non-native trees and shrubs in the planting of woodland.
(2) The use of straw bales at the edge of woodland or along hedgerows in order to provide wind-proof cover.
(3) The spreading of straw on rides within woodland of particular botanical interest.
(4) The distribution of feeding hoppers, release pens, watering troughs and other paraphernalia as a consequence of intensive pheasant rearing.
(5) The potential for predation on larvae of rare invertebrates such as marsh fritillary by pheasant poults near release pens.

Most of these problems are related to aesthetics although the use of non-native shrubs such as *Lonicera nitida* in the design of warm woodlands for pheasants should be avoided. *L. nitida* can become a problem to manage after a few years but its value has been in its relatively quick growth in comparison to native alternatives such as box. As an alternative many estates have introduced straw bales to the woodland edge which themselves have been heavily criticised on aesthetic grounds. In the heyday of pheasant shooting in Britain many estates planted rhododendron in their woods with the consequence that now many areas are impenetrable and little grows or lives under the huge bushes. This species is difficult to eradicate and has become a dominant feature of many woodlands originally planted for pheasants.

Snowberry is another species often planted in game preserves. Usually non-natives have an impoverished fauna even though they may satisfy the structural requirements of the pheasant shoot. Today however, as tighter controls are enforced on introductions and the value of native species is reiterated, the planting of *L. nitida* and snowberry may be difficult to justify.

The distribution of hand-rearing paraphernalia is merely a cosmetic consideration and a little care can usually remove this criticism. However, the use of straw on rides of high botanical interest has caused concern. Straw takes a particularly long time to break down, smothers plants and can upset the nutrient balance of the soil leading to alterations in the ride flora. Where there is an extensive ride system within the woodland less concern would be shown for a small amount of straw than where rides were few. However, it must be remembered that many of the rides are only cut for pheasants in the first place. If the same sites are used in successive years then damage may be restricted to a limited area of the wood.

SITE SAFEGUARDS AND GAME CONSERVATION

The total annual cost to the consumer and taxpayer of state support for agriculture in Britain has been put at £5 billion. Consider now state support for conservation. The government (1985 values) allocates 0.01% of public expenditure (0.005% of GDP) to support nature conservation − an amount which the NCC has calculated as the equivalent per capita of the price of a cup of tea (Lowe *et al*. 1986). If only we could direct some more of this money more profitably towards creating environments good for pheasant and other wildlife of conservation value! As Lowe *et al*. (1986) state in their book '*Countryside Conflicts*':

'Many of the Ministers in the House of Commons and indeed members of the House of Lords belong to the shooting fraternity. Greater awareness on their part ought to make them take more personal interest in countryside affairs but until now conservation and productive use of the land have been viewed in isolation. It is not possible to treat conservation as a separate self-contained unit during the planning of land-use. It has been pointed out that during the past

40 years this approach has failed. Conservation should no longer be regarded as a cosmetic frill or a palliative to the damaging impacts of productive and exploitative undertakings.' (Lowe *et al.* 1986)

The sportsman is nearer to a level of profitable exploitation of the land than is the conservationist. Large areas of land could be made both scenically more attractive and more valuable as wild-life habitats if the underlying sympathies for game were incorporated into the way we view land-use. Until now methods such as hand-rearing have necessarily detracted, to some extent, from managing habitats in the proper way. Short-term gain for agriculture has obscured long-term planning. Under the current trend of maximising profit from the land Lowe *et al.* (1986) paint a dismal picture for the future:

'All these pressures (striving for greater productivity, borrowing and inflated land prices) overwhelm any commitment to conservation, except where the landowner has sufficient spare capital, is aggressively and independently conservation minded, or is prepared to suffer real or paper losses by jumping off the intensification bandwagon. Unless these pressures and the policies that sustain them are overturned, conservation will continue to be seen as an expensive extra, costed in terms of lost production, focused largely on key sites, and dependent on public subsidy.'

The exception to this being management that brings in a potential profit, as is the case with the management of game.

In terms of featuring on key sites there has been a history of site designations and protection arrangements which prevent certain things being done to certain habitats of wildlife value. Such an array of bewildering names has been given to these areas or sites that the system has become very unwieldy. There are National Parks, areas of outstanding natural beauty, areas of great landscape beauty, Section 43 moor and heathland, green belts, heritage coasts, national scenic areas, country parks, regional parks, sites of special scientific interest, nature conservation review sites, national nature reserves, local nature reserves, forest nature reserves, environmentally sensitive areas, and special protection areas. Try to administer that lot − and we see the problem faced by conservation organisations today.

One solution to ensure protection is for conservation bodies to purchase the land. Voluntary conservation organisations now own about 300 000 ha, some 1.5% of the total area of the UK. And yet the rest, the vast majority of land, is that which in many instances is used for shooting. The purchase of areas of particular conservation interest is only a limited solution. We must recognise that the cost of permanent management agreements over large areas of land is formidably prohibitive. The answer is to give better advice to those who derive profit from the land. Game, and particularly pheasants, offer a means of achieving better conservation practice in the countryside as a whole.

References

Allen, D.L. 1941. *Rose Lake Wildlife Experimental Station Second Annual Report 1940−41*. State Department of Conservation, Lansing. Michigan. 365 pp.

Allen, D.L. 1947. Hunting as a limitation to Michigan pheasant populations. *Journal of Wildlife Management* 11:232−243.

Allen, D.L. 1956. The management outlook. In: *Pheasants in North America*. Chapter 9. Stackpole and the Wildlife Management Institute, Harrisburg, USA.

Allen, G.M. 1962. *Birds and Their Attributes*. 1st Print., 1926; Repr. 1962. Dover Publications, New York.

Anderson, W.L. 1964. Survival and reproduction of pheasants released in Southern Illinois. *Journal of Wildlife Management* 28:254−264.

Andrews, J. and Smart, N. 1985. *Birds and Broadleaves Handbook*. RSPB, The Lodge, Sandy, Beds. 128 pp.

Bailey, E.D. and Ralph, K.M. 1975. The effects of embryonic exposure to pheasant vocalisations in later call identification by chicks. *Canadian Journal of Zoology* 53:1028−1034.

Ball, K.E. 1950. Breeding behaviour of the ring-necked pheasant on Pelee Island, Ontario. *Canadian Field Naturalist* 64:201−207.

Barash, D.P. 1978. Sociobiology of rape in mallards (*Anas platyrhynchos*); responses of the mated male. *Science* 197:788−789.

Baskett, T.S. 1941. Production of pheasants in North Central Iowa in 1939. *Journal of Wildlife Management* 5:158−173.

Baskett, T.S. 1947. Nesting and production of the ring-necked pheasant in North Central Iowa. *Ecological Monographs* 17:1−30.

Batt, B.J.D. and Prince H.H. 1979. Laying date, clutch size and egg weight of captive mallard. *Condor* 81:35−41.

Baxter, W.L. and Wolfe, C.W. 1973. Life history and ecology of the ring-necked pheasant in Nebraska. *Nebraska Game and Parks Commission Technical Publication* 58.

Bealey, C.E. and Ludolf, I.C. 1988. The effects of woodland management for pheasants on the ground flora. *Game Conservancy Annual Review* 19:173−175.

Bengtson, S.-A. 1972. Reproduction and fluctuations in size of duck populations at Lake Myvatn, Iceland. *Oikos* 23:55−58.

Birkhead, T.R. 1979. Mate guarding in the magpie. *Animal Behaviour* 27:866−874.

Boatman, N.D. 1987. Selective grass weed control in cereal headlands to encourage game and wildlife. *1987 British Crop Protection Conference—Weeds* 1:277—284.

Bourne, W.R.P. 1957. The Breeding Birds of Bermuda. *Ibis*, 99:94.

Brady, S.J. 1987. Seizing wildlife opportunities within federal agricultural programs. *Proceedings of 49th Midwest Fish and Wildlife Conference*. Milwaukee, Wisconsin, 5—9 December 1987.

Bray, R.P. 1967. Mortality rates of released pheasants. *Game Research Association Annual Report* 7:14—33.

Breitenbach, R.P., Nagra, C.L. and Meyer, R.K. 1965 Studies of incubation and broody behaviour in the pheasant (*Phasianus colchicus*). *Animal Behaviour* 13:143—148.

Brennan, E. 1981. An investigation of the release of reared pheasant poults into a habitat containing a resident population. Unpub. MSc. (Ag.) Thesis National University of Ireland.

Bruning, D.F. 1974. Social structure and reproductive behaviour in the greater rhea. *Living Bird* 13:251—294.

Buckland, S.T. 1981. 'RECAP'. Program for the modified analysis of the Jolly-Seber capture-recapture model. *University of Aberdeen Technical Report No. 3*.

Buckland, S.T., Rowley, I. and Williams, D.A. 1983. Estimation of survival from repeated sightings of tagged galahs. *Journal of Animal Ecology* 52:563—573.

Bump, G. 1941. The introduction and transplantation of gamebirds and mammals into the State of New York. *Transactions of the North American Wildlife Conference* 5:409—420.

Bump, G. 1968. Exotics and the role of the State-Federal Foreign Game Investigations Program. In: *Proceedings of the Symposium Introduction Exotic Animals: Ecological and Socioeconomic Considerations*. Caesar Kleberg Research Program in Wildlife Ecology, College of Agriculture. Texas A and M University, Texas. pp. 5—8.

Burger, G.V. 1964. Survival of ring-necked pheasants released on a Wisconsin shooting preserve. *Journal of Wildlife Management* 28: 711—721.

Burger, G.V. 1987. 100 years of ring-necks: an updated historical perspective on pheasants in America. *Proceedings of 49th Midwest Fish and Wildlife Conference* Milwaukee, Wisconsin, 5—9 December 1987.

Buss, I.O. and Swanson, C.V. 1950. Some effects of weather on pheasant reproduction in southeastern Washington. *Transactions of the North American Wildlife Conference* 14:354—378.

Carl, G.C. and Guiguet, C.J. 1958. Alien animals in British Columbia. Handbook No.14. *British Columbia Provincial Museum*, Victoria, BC 94 pp.

Caum, E.L. 1933. The exotic birds of Hawaii. *Occasional Papers of the Bernice P. Bishop Museum* 10:1—55.

Cheng, K.M., Shoffner, R.N., Phillips, R.E. and Lee, F.B. 1978. Mate preference in wild and domesticated (game farm) mallard (*Anas platyrhynchos*) 1: Initial preference. *Animal Behaviour* 26:996—1003.

Cheng, K.M., Shoffner, R.N., Phillipps, R.E. and Lee, F.B. 1979. Mate preference in wild and domesticated (game garm) mallard (*Anas platyrhynchos*) 2: Pairing success. *Animal Behaviour* 27:214−222.

Cheng, T. 1964. *China's Economic Fauna*. US Department of Commerce. Office of Technical Services, Washington, USA.

Christensen, G.C. 1963. Exotic Game Bird Introductions into Nevada. *Nevada Fish and Game Commission Biological Bulletin* 3.

Christensen, G.C. 1967. The Status of Nevada's Exotic Bird Program. *Proceedings of the Conference of the Western Association of State Game and Fish Commissions*. Honolulu, Hawaii. July 16−20, 1967: 84−93.

Christian, J.J. 1956. Adrenal and reproductive responses to population size in mice from freely growing populations. *Ecology* 37:258−273.

Cobham, Resource Consultants 1983. *Countryside Sports: Their Economic Significance*. The Standing Conference on Countryside Sports. 45 pp.

Collinge, W.E. 1927. *The Food of Some British Wild Birds*. The Museum, York.

Colson, R.B. 1968. New Pheasant Introductions: A Progress Report. *Conservationist* 23:2−4.

Conway, G. 1982. *Pesticide Resistance and World Food Reduction*. Imperial College Centre for Environmental Technology. 143 pp.

Cramp, S. and Simmons, K.E.L. (Eds) 1980. *The Birds of the Western Palearctic*. Vol. 2. Oxford University Press, Oxford, UK.

Dahlgren, R.B. 1987. Pheasant distribution and abundance 1930−1936. *Proceedings of 49th Midwest Fish and Wildlife Conference*. Milwaukee, Wisconsin, 5−9 December 1987.

Dale, F.H. 1951. Sex ratios in pheasant research and management. *Journal of Wildlife Management* 16:156−163.

Dalke, P.D. 1937. Food habits of adult pheasants based on crop analyses. *Ecology* 18:199−213.

Delacour, J. 1977. *Pheasants of the World*. 2nd Ed. World Pheasant Association and Saiga, Surrey, UK.

Dementiev, G.P. and Gladkov, N.A. 1967. *Birds of the Soviet Union*. Vol. 4. Israel Program for Scientific Translations, Jerusalem.

Dijkstra, C., Vuursteen, L., Daan, S. and Masman, D. 1982. Clutch size and laying date in the kestrel (*Falco tinnunculus*). Effect of supplementary food. *Ibis* 124:210−230.

Dixon, K.R. and Chapman, J.A. 1980. Harmonic mean measure of animal activity areas. *Ecology* 61:1040−1044.

Dumke, R.T. and Pils, C.M. 1973. Mortality of radio-tagged pheasants on the Waterloo wildlife area. *Technical Bulletin of the Wisconsin Department of Natural Resources* 72. 52 pp.

Dumke, R.T. and Pils, C.M. 1979. Renesting and dynamics of nest site selection by Wisconsin pheasants. *Journal of Wildlife Management* 43:705−716.

Edwards, W.R. 1962. Hen pheasant kill by hunting. *Game Research in Ohio* 1:26−27.

Edwards, W.R. 1963. Proportionate harvest of ring-neck pheasant cocks and hens. *Game Research in Ohio* 2:11–22.

Edwards, W.R., Mikolaj, P.J. and Leite E.A. 1964. Implications from winter–spring weights of pheasants. *Journal of Wildlife Management* 28:270–279.

Einarsen, A.S. 1942. Specific results from ring-necked pheasant studies in the Pacific Northwest. *Transactions of the North American Wildlife Conference* 12:130–138.

Elliott, P.F. 1975. Longevity and the evolution of polygamy. *American Naturalist* 109:281–287.

Ellis, J.A. and Anderson, W.L. 1963. Attempts to establish pheasants in southern Illinois. *Journal of Wildlife Management* 27:225–239.

Erikson, A.B., Vesall, D.B. and Rollings, C.T. 1951. Minnesota's most important gamebird, the pheasant. Facts and figures on pheasant studies 1939–1950. *The Flicker* 23:23–49.

Erlinge, S., Frylestram, B., Göransson G., Hogstedt, G., Liberg, O., Loman, J. Nilsson, I.N., Von Schatz, T. and Sylven, M. 1984. Predation on brown hare and ring-necked pheasant populations in southern Sweden. *Holarctic Ecology* 7:300–304.

Ford, H.A. 1987. Bird communities on habitat islands in England. *Bird Study* 34:205–218.

Frömberg, I. and Helgee, A. 1985. Social dominance and reproductive resources in male pheasants. *Proceedings of the XVIIth Congress of the International Union of Game Biologists*: 17–21.

Fuller, R.J. 1982. *Bird Habitats in Britain*. T.A. Poyser. 320 pp.

Gabrielson, I.N. and Lincoln F.C. 1959. *The Birds of Alaska*. Stackpole, Pennsylvania.

Garnier-Ruffer, J. 1977. *The Big-Shots: Edwardian Shooting Parties*. Debrett's Peerage Ltd, London.

Garson, P.J., Pleszczynska W.K. and Holm, C.H. 1981. The 'polygyny threshold' model: a reassessment. *Canadian Journal of Zoology* 59:902–910.

Gates, J.M. 1966. Renesting behaviour in the ring-necked pheasant. *Wilson Bulletin* 78:309–315.

Gates, J.M. 1971. The ecology of a Wisconsin pheasant population. PhD thesis. University of Wisconsin, Madison. 912 pp.

Gates, J.M. and Hale, J.B. 1974. Seasonal movements, winter habitat use and population distribution in an East Central Wisconsin pheasant population. *Technical Bulletin of the Wisconsin Department of Natural Resources* 76:1–55.

Gates, J.M. and Woehler, E.E. 1968. Winter weight loss related to subsequent weights and reproduction in penned pheasant hens. *Journal of Wildlife Management* 32:234–247.

Geis, A.D. and Elbert, L.H. 1956. Relation of tail length of ring-necked pheasants to harem size. *Auk* 73:289.

Gill, M.F. 1978. Breeding of wild pheasant. *Game Conservancy Annual Review* 9:29–34.

Gindre, R. 1974. Population dynamics of a mixed ring-necked pheasant population on a shooting area in France. *Proceedings of the XIth Congress of the International Union of Game Biologists*: 235–244.

Ginn, W.E. 1955. The ring-necked pheasant. In: *Wildlife Restoration 1939–55*. (Ed. Allen, J.M.). Indiana Department of Conservation, Pittman-Robertson Bulletin No. 3. 240 pp.

Godfrey, W.E. 1966. *The Birds of Canada*. National Museum of Canada, Bulletin 230.

Göransson, G. 1975. Duvhökens (*Accipiter gentilis*) betydelse för vinterdödligheten hos fasaner (*Phasianus colchicus*). *Anser* 14:11–22.

Göransson, G. 1980. Dynamics, reproduction and social organisation in pheasant (*Phasianus colchicus*) populations in South Scandinavia. PhD Dissertation, Department of Animal Ecology, Lund, Sweden.

Gottschalk, J.S. 1967. The Introduction of Exotic Animals into the United States. In: *Proceedings Xth Technical Meeting IUCN 1966, Part III Changes Due to Introduced Species*, Morges, Switzerland 9:124–140.

Gray, N. 1986. *Woodland Management for Pheasants and Wildlife*. David & Charles. London. 176 pp.

Green, R.E. 1984. The feeding ecology and survival of partridge chicks (*Alectoris rufa* and *Perdix perdix*) on arable farmland in East Anglia, UK. *Journal of Applied Ecology* 21:817–830.

Greenberg, R.E., Etter, S.L. and Anderson, W.L. 1972. Evaluation of proximal primary feather criteria for ageing wild pheasants. *Journal of Wildlife Management* 36:700–705.

Grey, Viscount, 1927. *The Charm of Birds*. Hodder and Stoughton, London, UK.

Guild, E. 1938. Tahitian aviculture: acclimatisation of foreign birds. *Avicultural Magazine* 3:8–11.

Hachisuka, M. and Udagawa, T. 1951. Contribution to the ornithology of Formosa. *Quarterly Journal of the Taiwan Museum* 4:1–180.

Haensly, T.F., Meyers, S.M., Crawford, J.A. and Castillo, W.J. 1985. Treatments affecting post-release survival and productivity of pen reared ring-necked pheasants. *Wildlife Society Bulletin* 13:521–528.

Hall, M. 1981. *Butterfly Monitoring Scheme*. Institute of Terrestrial Ecology.

Hammer, M., Koie, M. and Sparck, R. 1958. Investigations on the food of partridges, pheasants and black grouse in Denmark. *Danish Review of Game Biology* 3:183–208.

Hanson, L.E. and Progulske, D.R. 1973. Movement and cover preferences of pheasants in South Dakota. *Journal of Wildlife Management* 37:454–461.

Hanson, W.R. 1970. Pheasant nesting and concealment in hayfields. *Auk* 87:714–719.

Hanson, W.R. and Labinsky, R.F. 1964. Association of pheasants with vegetation in East-central Illinois. *Transactions of the North American Wildlife Conference* 29:295–306.

Harper, H.T. 1960. The effects of a three year limited hen season on pheasant populations in California, 1955–1957. *Proceedings of the Western Association State Game and Fish Commission* 40:168–176.

Harper, H.T. Chester, C.M. and Shaffer, D.E. 1951. Effects of hunting pressure and game farm stocking on pheasant populations in the Sacramento Valley, California 1946–1949. *California Fish and Game* 37:141–176.

Hartman, F.E. and Scheffer, D.E. 1971. Population dynamics and hunter harvest of ring-necked pheasant populations in Pennsylvania's primary range. *Transactions of the North East Section of the Wildlife Society* 28, 179–205.

Heinz, G. 1973. Responses of ring-necked pheasant chicks (*Phasianus colchicus*) to conspecific calls. *Animal Behaviour* 21:1–9.

Hellmayr, C.E. 1932. Birds of Chile. *Museum of Natural History, Chicago Zoological Service* 19:308.

Hensler, G.L. and Nichols, J.D. 1981. The Mayfield method of estimating nesting success: a model, estimators and simulation results. *Wilson Bulletin* 93:42–53.

Hessler, E., Tester, J.R. Siniff, D.B. and Nelson, M.M. 1970. A biotelemetrical study of survival of pen-reared pheasants released in selected habitats. *Journal of Wildlife Management* 34:267–274.

Hiatt, R.W. and Fisher, H.I. 1947. The reproductive cycle of pheasants in Montana. *Auk* 64:528–548.

Hill, D.A. 1984. *Report of the Pheasant Project*. The Game Conservancy, Fordingbridge, UK.

Hill, D.A. 1984b. Population regulation in the mallard. *Journal of Animal Ecology* 53:192–202.

Hill, D.A. 1985. The feeding ecology and survival of pheasant chicks on arable farmland. *Journal of Applied Ecology* 22:645–654.

Hill, D.A. (in press.) Population dynamics of avocets (*Recurvirostra avosetta*) breeding in Britain. *Journal of Animal Ecology*.

Hill, D.A. and Carter, N. 1988. Population simulation models as an aid to gamebird management. In: *The Ecology and Management of Gamebirds*. (Eds P.J. Hudson and M.R.W. Rands). Blackwell Scientific Publications, Oxford.

Hill, D.A. and Edwards, J. 1986. The compatability of pheasant management and woodland conservation with emphasis on southern English coppice. Paper submitted to the 'Recreation Ecology Research Group', Wye College, Kent, April 1986.

Hill, D.A. and Ridley, M.W. 1987. Sexual segregation in winter, spring dispersal and habitat use in the pheasant. *Journal of Zoology* 212:657–668.

Hill, D.A. and Robertson, P.A. 1986. Hand-reared pheasants: How do they compare with wild birds. *Game Conservancy Annual Review* 17:76–84.

Hill, D.A. and Robertson, P.A. 1987a. The role of radiotelemetry in the study of Galliformes. *Journal of the World Pheasant Association* 12:81–92.

Hill, D.A. and Robertson, P.A. 1987b. Hand reared pheasants: how they affect productivity. *Game Conservancy Annual Review* 18:65–69.

Hill, D.A. and Robertson, P.A. (in press). The comparative breeding success of wild and hand-reared pheasants (*Phasianus colchicus*). *Journal of Wildlife Management*.

Hudson, P.J. 1985. *Red Grouse, The Biology and Management of a Wild Gamebird*. The Game Conservancy Trust, Fordingbridge, UK. 249 pp.

Hudson, P.J. 1986. The effect of a parasitic nematode on the breeding production of red grouse. *Journal of Animal Ecology* 55:85–94.

Jacobs, J. 1974. Quantitative measurement of food selection. A modification of the forage ratio and Ivlev's electivity index. *Oecologia (berl.)* 14:413–417.

Janson, R., Hartkorn, F. and Greene, R. 1971. Ring-necked pheasant. In: *Game Management in Montana*. (Eds T.W. Mussehl and F.W. Howell). Montana Fish and Game Department, Helena, Montana, Chapter 18:153–159.

Jarvis, R.L. and Engbring, J. 1976. Survival and reproduction of wild game farm pheasants in Western Oregon. *Northwestern Science* 50: 222–230.

Johnsgard, P.A. 1986. *Pheasants of the World*. Oxford University Press.

Jorgensen, S.E. 1986. *Fundamentals of Ecological Modelling*. Elsevier, Amsterdam. 389 pp.

Kenward, R.E. 1977. Predation on released pheasants (*Phasianus colchicus*) by goshawks (*Accipiter gentilis*) in Central Sweden. *Viltrevy* 10:79–109.

Kenward, R.E. 1978. Hawks and doves: Factors affecting success and selection in goshawk attacks on woodpigeon. *Journal of Animal Ecology* 47:449–460.

Kenward, R.E., Marcström, V. and Karlbom, M. 1981. Goshawk winter ecology in Swedish pheasant habitats. *Journal of Wildlife Management* 45:397–408.

Kenward, R.E. 1986. Problems of goshawk predation on pigeons and other game. *Proceedings of International Ornithological Congress* 18:666–678.

Kenward, R.E. 1987. Wildlife radio-tagging: equipment, field techniques and data analysis. Academic Press, London. 222 pp.

Kessler, F. 1962. Measurement of nest attentiveness in the ring-necked pheasant. *Auk* 79:702–705.

Kimball, J.W. 1948. Pheasant population characteristics and trends in the Dakotas. *Transactions of the North American Wildlife Conference* 13:291–314.

King, J.R. 1974. Seasonal allocation of time and energy resources in birds. In: *Avian Energetics* (Ed. R.A. Paynter) pp. 4–85. Nuttall Ornithological Club, Cambridge, Mass., USA.

Klopfer, P. 1963. Behavioural aspects of habitat selection; the role of early experience. *Wilson Bulletin* 75:15–22.

Koch, L. 1956. *The Encyclopaedia of British Birds*, Waverley Book Co., London.

Kozicky, E.L. 1957. Juvenile ring-necked pheasant mortality and cover utilisation in Iowa. *Iowa State College Journal of Science* 26:85–93.

Krapu, G.L. 1979. Nutrition of female dabbling ducks during reproduction. In: *Waterfowl and Wetlands – An Integrated Review*. (Ed. Bookhout, T.A.) Proceedings of the 1977 Symposium of the Wildlife Society, Madison.

Kuck, T.L., Dahlgren, R.B. and Progulske, D.R. 1970. Movement and behaviour of hen pheasants during the nesting season. *Journal of Wildlife Management* 34:626–630.

Labinsky, R.F. and Jackson, G.L. 1969. Production and weights of eggs laid by yearling, 2nd and 3rd year old pheasants. *Journal of Wildlife Management* 33:718–721.

Lachlan, C. and Bray, R.P. 1973. A study of an unmanaged pheasant population at Brownsea Island, Dorset. *Proceedings of the Xth Congress of the International Union of Game Biologists*: 609–617.

Lachlan, C. and Bray, R.P. 1976. Habitat selection by cock pheasants in spring. *Journal of Applied Ecology* 13:691–704.

Lack, P. 1986. *Atlas of Wintering Birds in Britain and Ireland.* T.A. Poyser. 447 pp.

Lance, A.N. 1973. Releases of pen-reared red grouse (*Lagopus l. scoticus*) to restock breeding populations in Ireland. *Proceedings of the XIth Congress of the International Union of Game Biologists* 225–229.

Latham, R.M. 1947. Differential ability of male and female gamebirds to withstand starvation and climatic extremes. *Journal of Wildlife Management* 11:139–149.

Leopold, A.S. 1949. *The Pheasant Kill on the Conway Ranch — 1947 and 1948.* University of California, Berkeley. 14 pp.

Lehtonen, L. 1975. Fasaanin talvisesta vuorokausirytmiikasta. *Suomen Riista* 26:97–107.

Lever, C. 1977. *The Naturalised Animals of the British Isles.* Hutchinson & Co., London.

Linder, R.L., Lyon, D.L. and Agee, C.P. 1960. An analysis of pheasant nesting in South Central Nebraska. *Transactions of the North American Wildlife Conference* 25:214–230.

Lloyd, D.E.B. 1976. *Avian Predation of Reared Pheasants.* The Game Conservancy, Fordingbridge, UK.

Long, J.L. 1981. *Introduced Birds of the World*, David & Charles, London.

Longrigg, R. 1977. *The English Squire and his Sport*, Michael Joseph, London, 320 pp.

Lorenz, K.Z. 1952. *King Soloman's Ring.* Methuen.

Lowe, P.R. 1933. The differential characters in the Tarso-metatarsi of *Gallus* and Phasianus as they bear on the problem of the introduction of the pheasant into Europe and the British Isles. *Ibis* 3:332–343.

Lowe, P., Cox, G., Macewen, M., O'Riordan, T., and Winter, M. 1986. *Countryside Conflicts, The Politics of Farming, Forestry and Conservation.* Gower/Temple-Smith. 378 pp.

Ludolf, I.C., Robertson, P.A. and Woodburn M.I.A. (in press). The Management of Lowland Woods to Encourage Pheasants: Effects on the Ground Flora.

Lyon, L.J. 1959. An evaluation of woody cover plantings as pheasant winter cover. *Transactions of the North American Wildlife Conference* 24: 277–289.

Macdonald, D.W. 1980. The red fox (*Vulpes vulpes*) as a predator upon earthworms. *Zeitschrift für Tierpsychologie* 52:171–200.

Macnamara, L.G. and Kozicky, E.L. 1949. Band returns from male ring-necked pheasants in New Jersey. *Journal of Wildlife Management* 13:286–294.

Majewska, B., Pielowski, Z., Serwatka, S. and Szott, M. 1979. Genetische und adaptative Eigenschaften des Zuchtmaterials zum Aussetzen von Fasanen. *Zeitschrift für Jagdwissenschaft* 25:212–226.

Mallette, R.D. and Harper, H.T. 1964. Population studies of ring-necked pheasants in California. *Californian Fish and Game* 37:141–175.

Matheson, C. 1963. The pheasant in Wales. *British Birds* 44:452–456.

Mayfield, H. 1961. Nesting success calculated from exposure. *Wilson Bulletin* 73:255–261.

Mayfield, H. 1975. Suggestions for calculating nest success. *Wilson Bulletin* 87:456−466.

McAttee, W.L. 1945. *The Ring-Necked Pheasant and its Management in North America*. The American Wildlife Institute, Washington DC. 320 pp.

McBride, G., Parker, I.P. and Foenander, F. 1969. The social organisation and behaviour of the feral domestic fowl. *Animal Behaviour Monographs* 2:127−181.

McCall, I. 1985. *Your Shoot. Gamekeepering and Management*. Black. 180 pp.

Meinertzhagen, R. 1912. On the birds of Mauritius. *Ibis* 82−108.

Meriggi, A. 1983. Territory, habitat preference and breeding success of a population of pheasants. *Avocetta* 7:1−12.

Merikallio, E. 1958. *Finnish Birds: Their Distribution and Numbers*. Helsingfors, Helsinki.

Mirza, Z.B. 1979. Cheer pheasant release programme in Pakistan. In: Pheasants in Asia 1979; *Proceedings of the 1st International Symposium on Pheasants in Asia*. Kathmandu, Nepal, 1979.

Mohler, L.L. 1951. Ratio of young to adult pheasants bagged in 1950 Nebraska. *Pittman-Robertson Quarterly Report*, April 1,1951. 333 pp.

Moreby, S.J. (in press). A key to the identification of arthropod fragments in the faeces of gamebird chicks. *Ibis*.

Murton, R.K., Westwood, N.J. and Isaacson, A.J., 1974. A study of wood-pigeon shooting: the exploitation of a natural animal population. *Journal of Applied Ecology* 11:61−81.

Myers, J.E. 1970. The ecology of the wild-trapped and transplanted ring-necked pheasant near Centre Hall, Pennsylvania. *Transactions of the North American Wildlife Conference* 35:216−220.

Myrberget, S. 1976. Merking av Fasan i Norge. *Sterna* 15:174−176.

Nazerenko, L.F. and Gurskii, I.G. 1963. The acclimatization of pheasants in the area Northwest of the Black Sea. *Ornitiologiya* 6:477−478.

Nelson, L.K. 1963. Introductions of the blackneck pheasant group and crosses into the South Eastern States. *Proceedings of the Conference of the South Eastern Association of State Game and Fish Commissions* 17:111−119.

Nelson, B.A. and Janson, R.G. 1949. Starvation of pheasants in South Dakota. *Journal of Wildlife Management* 13:308−309.

Neu, C.W., Byers, C.R. and Peek, J.M. 1974. A technique for analysis of utilisation-availability data. *Journal of Wildlife Management* 38: 541−545.

O'Connor, R.J. and Shrubb, M. 1986. *Farming and Birds*. Cambridge University Press.

O'Gorman, F. 1970. The development of game in Ireland. *Proceedings of the VIIIth Congress of the International Union of Game Biologists*: 387−396.

Orians, G.H. 1969. On the evolution of mating systems in birds and mammals. *American Naturalist* 103:589−603.

Oring, L.W. 1982. Avian mating systems. In: *Avian Biology* Vol. 6. (Ed. D.S. Farner, J.R. King and K.C. Parkes) pp. 1−92. Academic Press, New York, USA.

O'Rourke, F.J. 1970. *The Fauna of Ireland*. Mercier Press, Cork.

Overseas Trade Statistics HM Customs and Excise 1980. Taken from '*Country-side Sports – Their Economic Significance*' Survey by Cobham Resource Consultants (1983). The Standing Conference on Countryside Sports, 45 pp.

Paludan, K. 1958. Some results of marking experiments on pheasants from a Danish estate Kalö. *Danish Review of Game Biology* 3:169–181.

Pekic, B. 1962. Natural feeding of pheasants and its application to their artificial breeding. *Biological Institute of Beograda Monograph* 10:1–58.

Penrod, B., Dixon, M. and Smith, J. 1982. Renesting by ring-necked pheasants after loss of or separation from their first brood. *New York Fish and Game Journal* 29:209–210.

Peterken, G. 1981. *Woodland Conservation and Management*. Chapman & Hall. London. 328 pp.

Phillips, J.C. 1928. Wild birds introduced or transplanted in North America. *United States Department of Agriculture Technical Bulletin* 61:64 pp.

Pielowski, Z. 1981. Weitere Untersuchungen uber den Wert des Zuchtmaterials von Fasanen zum Aussetzen. *Zeitschrift für Jagdwissenschaft* 27:102–109.

Pollard, E. 1977. A method for assessing changes in the abundance of butterflies. *Biological Conservation* 12:115–124.

Potts, G.R. 1970. Recent changes in the farmland fauna with special reference to the decline in the grey partridge (*Perdix perdix*). *Bird Study* 17:145–166.

Potts, G.R. 1980. The effects of modern agriculture, nest predation and game management on the population ecology of partridges (*Perdix perdix*) and (*Alectoris rufa*). *Advances in Ecological Research* 11:1–82.

Potts, G.R. 1986. *The Partridge: Pesticides, Predation and Conservation*. Collins, London.

Potts, G.R. and Vickerman, G.P. 1974. Studies of the cereal ecosystem. *Advances in Ecological Research* 8:107–197.

Pulliainen, E. 1966. Fasaanin ravinnosta suomessa. *Suomen Riista* 19: 113–125.

Rackham, O. 1978. *Trees and Woodland in the British Landscape*. Dent.

Rands, M.R.W. 1985. Pesticide use on cereals and the survival of grey partridge chicks: a field experiment. *Journal of Applied Ecology* 22:49–54.

Rainey, A. 1973. *Mosaics in Roman Britain*. London, Hutchinson.

Reynolds, J.C. and Tapper, S.C. 1986. Foxes and their habitats. *Game Conservancy Annual Review* 18:87–93.

Ridley, M.W. 1983. The mating system of the pheasant *Phasianus colchicus*. Unpub. DPhil. Thesis, University of Oxford.

Ridley, M.W. 1986. The cheer pheasant re-introduction project: a discussion paper. *Proceedings of the IIIrd International Symposium on Pheasants in Asia*. Thailand, January 1986.

Ridley, M.W. and Hill, D.A. 1987. Social organisation in the pheasant: harem formation, mate selection and the role of mate guarding. *Journal of Zoology* 211:619–630.

Robertson, P.A. 1985a. Habitat selection and the relative distributions of wild and released pheasants (*Phasianus colchicus*) as determined by winter trapping. *Journal of the World Pheasant Association* 10: 87–99.

Robertson, P.A. 1985b. Aging Irish pheasants by measurement of their proximal primaries. *Irish Birds* 3:71–74.

Robertson, P.A. 1986. The ecology and management of hand-reared and wild pheasants (*Phasianus colchicus*) in Ireland. Unpub. PhD Thesis, National University of Ireland.

Robertson, P.A. 1988a. Pheasant management in small broadleaved woodlands. In: *Wildlife management in forests*. Proceedings of the ICF discussion meeting, 3–5 April 1987: 25–33.

Robertson, P.A. 1988b. The survival of released pheasants (*Phasianus colchicus*) in Ireland. *Journal of Zoology* 214:683–695.

Robertson, P.A. and Hill, D.A. (in press). A bird in the bush is worth four in the hand: hand-rearing and the productivity of pheasants in the wild. *Proceedings of the XVIIIth Congress of the International Union of Game Biologists.*

Robertson, P.A., Hill, D.A. and Raw, K.A. 1985. Variations in body weight and tarsal dimensions of English and Irish pheasants with notes on ring sizes. *Ringing and Migration* 6:119–121.

Robertson, P.A. and Rosenberg, A.A. 1988. Harvesting gamebirds. In: *Gamebird Ecology: Principles of Management and Conservation* (Eds P.J. Hudson, and M.R.W. Rands). Blackwell, London.

Robertson, P.A. and Whelan, J. 1987a. The food of the red fox (*Vulpes vulpes*) in Co. Kildare, Ireland. *Journal of Zoology* 213:740–743.

Robertson, P.A. and Whelan, J. 1987b. The ecology and management of wild and hand-reared pheasants in Ireland. *Irish Birds* 3:427–518.

Robertson, P.A., Woodburn, M.I.A. and Hill, D.A. (in press.) The effect of woodland management for pheasants on the abundance of butterflies. *Biological Conservation*.

Robertson, W.B. 1958. Investigations of ring-necked pheasants in Illinois. *Illinois Division of Game Management Technical Bulletin* 1:1–137.

Robinson, L.H. 1969. Introduction of exotic game birds in South Carolina. *Proceedings of the Conference of the South Eastern Association of State Game and Fisheries Commissions* 23: 152–159.

Rubel, E.W. 1970. Effects of early experience on fear behaviour of *Coturnix coturnix. Animal Behaviour.* 18:427–433.

Rushen, J. 1982. The peck orders of chickens: how do they develop and why are they linear? *Animal Behaviour* 30:1129–1137.

Russell, K.R. 1974. An unsuccessful artificial nesting structure for pheasants. *Journal of Wildlife Management* 38:372–375.

Salzen, E.A. 1963. Imprinting and the immobility reactions of domestic fowl. *Animal Behaviour* 11:66–71.

Sandfort, W. 1963. We can have more pheasants. *Colorado Outdoors* 12:1–6.

Scott, M.L., Holm, E.R. and Reynolds, R.E. 1955. The effect of diet on the ability of young pheasant chicks to withstand the stress of cold drenching rain. *Poultry Science* 34:949–956.

Seubert, J.L. 1952. Observations on the re-nesting behaviour of the ring-necked pheasant. *Transactions of the North American Wildlife Conference* 17:305–329.

Severinghaus, S.R., Mirza, A.B. and Asghar, M. 1979. The selection of a release site for the re-introduction of cheer pheasants in Pakistan. *Journal of the World Pheasant Association* 4:11–115.

Shaw, W.T. 1908. *The China or Denny Pheasant in Oregon with Notes on the Native Grouse of the Pacific North West.* J.B. Lippincott and Co., Philadelphia and London.

Sheail, J. 1985. *Pesticides and Nature Conservation: The British Experience 1950–1975*. Clarendon Press, Oxford.

Shoard, M. 1980. *The Theft of the Countryside*. Temple Smith, London.

Sibley, R.M. 1981. Strategies of digestion and defecation. In: *Physiological Ecology* (Eds C.R. Townsend and P. Callow). Blackwell Scientific Publications, Oxford. pp.109–139.

Siegfried, W.R. 1978. Social behaviour of the African comb duck. *Living Bird* 17:85–104.

Silverstein, A. and Silverstein V. 1974. *Animal Invaders: The Story of Imported Wildlife*. Atheneum, New York.

Simpson, J. 1907. *Game and Game Coverts*. Pawson and Brailsford, London. 83 pp.

Snyder, W.D. 1974. Pheasant use of roadsides for nesting in north east Colorado. *Colorado Division of Wildlife Special Report* 36. 24 pp.

Snyder, W.D. 1984. Ring-necked pheasant nesting ecology and wheat farming in the High Plains. *Journal of Wildlife Management* 48:878– 888.

Sonerud, G.A. 1985. Brood movements in grouse and waders as defence against win-stay search in predators. *Oikos* 44:287–300.

Sotherton, N.W., Dover, J.W. and Rands, M.R.W. (in press). Pesticides exclusion strips in Great Britain. *Proceedings of Fourth European Ecology Symposium: Ecological implications of contemporary agriculture*. (Eds A. Quispel and H. Eysackers).

Sotherton, N.W. and Moreby, S.J. 1984. Contact toxicity of some foliar fungicide sprays to three species of polyphagous predators found in cereal fields. *Tests of Agrochemicals and Cultivars* No.5 (*Annals of Applied Biology*) 104: 16–17.

Sotherton, N.W., Moreby, S.J. and Langley, M.G. 1987. The effects of the foliar fungicide pyrazophos on beneficial arthropods in barley fields. *Annals of Applied Biology* 111:75–87.

Sotherton. N.W., Rands, M.R.W. and Moreby, S.J. 1985. Comparison of herbicide treated and untreated headlands for the survival of game and wildlife. *1985 British Crop Protection Conference – Weeds* 3: 991–998.

Stokes, A.W. 1954. Population studies of the ring-necked pheasants on Pelee Island, Ontario. *Technical Bulletin of the Wildlife Service No.4*. Ontario Department of Lands and Forests.

Stokes, A.W. 1968. An eight-year study of a northern Utah pheasant population. *Journal of Wildlife Management* 32:867–874.

Taber, R.D. 1949. Observations on the breeding behaviour of the ring-necked pheasant. *Condor* 51:153–175.

Tester, J.R. and Olson, L. 1959. Experimental starvation of pheasants. *Journal of Wildlife Management* 23:304–309.

Thaler, E. 1986. Studies on the behaviour of some *Phasianidae* chicks at the Alpenzoo–Innsbruck. *Proceedings of the IIIrd International Symposium on Pheasants in Asia*. Thailand, January 1986.

Thomas, J. and Webb, N. 1984. *Butterflies of Dorset*. Dorset Natural History and Archaeological Society, Dorchester, 128 pp.

Thomas, V.G. 1986. Diet and gut properties of pheasants in relation to restocking success. *Journal of the World Pheasant Association* 11: 67–75.

Thomson, G.M. 1922. *The Naturalisation of Animals and Plants in New Zealand*. Cambridge University Press, New Zealand.

Townsend, C.W. 1963. Ring-necked pheasant habits. In: *Life histories of North American Gallinaceous Birds*. (Ed. A.C. Bent). Dover Pub. Inc. New York.

Trautman, C.G. 1960. Evaluation of pheasant nesting habitat in east South Dakota. *Proceedings of the North American Wildlife Conference*. 25:202−213.

Tuttle, H.J. 1963. Japanese Green and Kalij Pheasants in Virginia. *Proceedings of the Conference of the South Eastern Association of State Game and Fish Commission* 17:121−123.

Twining, H. 1946. Life history and management of the ring-necked pheasant in California. *Pittman-Robertson Quarterly Report* 6:145−146.

Underhill-Day, J.C. (in prep.). The effect of predation by marsh harriers (*Circus aeruginosus*) on the survival of ducklings and gamebird chicks.

Verner, J. 1964. Evolution of polygamy in the long-billed marsh wren. *Evolution* 18:252−261.

Wagner, F.H. 1957. Late summer mortality in the pheasant hen. *Proceedings of the North American Wildlife Conference* 22:301−315.

Wagner, F.H., Besadny, C.D. and Kabat, C. 1965. Population ecology and management of Wisconsin pheasants. *Winconsin Conservation Department Technical Bulletin* 34, 168 pp.

Warner, R.E. 1979. Use of cover by pheasant broods in East Central Illinois, USA. *Journal of Wildlife Management* 43:334−346.

Warner, R.E. 1984. Effects of changing agriculture on ring-necked pheasant brood movements in Illinois. *Journal of Wildlife Management* 48:1014−1018.

Warner, R.W. Darda, D.M. and Baker, D.H. 1982. Effects of dietary protein level and environmental temperature stress on growth of young ring-necked pheasants. *Poultry Science* 61:673−676.

Westerskov, K. 1956. Productivity of New Zealand pheasant populations. *New Zealand Department of Internal Affairs Wildlife Publications* 408:1−144.

Westerskov, K. 1962. The pheasant in New Zealand. *New Zealand Department of Internal Affairs Wildlife Publication* 40, 1955, Repr. 1962:1−35.

Wetmore, A. 1965. *The Birds of the Republic of Panama*. Washington.

Williams, G.R. 1960. The Birds of the Pitcairn Islands, Central South Pacific Ocean. *Ibis* 102:58−70.

Wilson, P.J. 1986. Botanical conservation in cereal headlands. *1986 Game Conservancy Annual Review* 18:112−116.

Wilson, P.J. 1987. An investigation into the effects of selective herbicide use in cereal field crop margins on the weed flora: the results of the Cereals and Gamebirds Research Project botanical survey, 1986. Unpub. Game Conservancy Report, February 1987

Wishart, W. and Knapton, R.W. 1978. Male pintails defending females from rape. *Auk* 95:186−187.

Wittenberger, J.F. 1978. The evolution of mating systems in birds and mammals. In: *Handbook of Behavioural Neurobiology vol. 3: Social Behaviour and Communication* (Eds P. Marler and J. Vandenbergh). Plenum, New York, USA. pp.271−349.

Wollard, L.L., Sparrowe R.D. and Chambers, G.D. 1977. Evaluation of a Korean pheasant introduction in Missouri. *Journal of Wildlife Management* 41:616−623.

Wood, A.K. and Brotherson, J.D. 1981. Microenvironment and nest site selection by ring-necked pheasants in Utah. *Great Basin Naturalist* 41:457–460.

Woodward, A.E., Vohra, P. and Snyder, R.L. 1977. Effects of dietary protein levels in the diet on the growth of pheasants. *Poultry Science*, 56:1492–1500.

Woodward, A.E., Abplanalp, H., Pisenti, J.M. and Snyder, L.R. 1983. Inbreeding effects on reproductive traits in the ring-necked pheasant. *Poultry Science* 62:1725–1730.

Worsely, A. 1974. Long-term effects of imprinting exposure upon breed discriminatory behaviour in chickens: I. Imprinting to peers ('peerprinting') *Zeitschrift für Tierpsychologie* 35:1–9.

Yanushevich, A.I. 1966. Acclimatization of animals in the USSR. In *Proceedings of the conference on Acclimatised Animals in the USSR, Frunze, 10–15 May, 1963*. Israel Program for Scientific Translations.

Yapp, W.B. 1983. Gamebirds in medieval England. *Ibis* 125:218–221.

Index